PARTICLE WAVES AND DEFORMATION IN CRYSTALLINE SOLIDS

PARTICLE WAVES
AND DEFORMATION
IN CRYSTALLINE SOLIDS

Edwin R. Fitzgerald

The Johns Hopkins University
Baltimore, Maryland

Interscience Publishers
A Division of John Wiley & Sons
New York • London • Sydney

Line drawings for the figures
by the author

Dedicated to Carolyn

Listen again. One Evening at the Close
Of Ramazan, ere the better Moon arose,
    In that old Potter's Shop I stood alone
With the clay Population round in Rows.

And strange to tell, among that Earthen Lot
Some could articulate, while others not:
    And suddenly one more impatient cried—
"Who *is* the Potter, pray, and who the Pot?"

Then said another—"Surely not in vain
My substance from the common Earth was ta'en,
    That He who subtly wrought me into Shape
Should stamp me back to common Earth again."

Another said—"Why, ne'er a peevish Boy
Would break the Bowl from which he drank in Joy;
    Shall He that *made* the Vessel in pure Love
And Fansy, in an after Rage destroy!"

None answer'd this; but after Silence spake
A Vessel of a more ungainly Make:
    "They sneer at me for leaning all awry;
What? did the Hand then of the Potter shake?"

THE RUBAIYAT OF OMAR KHAYYAM
EDWARD FITZGERALD TRANSLATION

PREFACE

The idea that there is a close connection between particle waves and the macroscopic deformation of solids will be surprising to many and distasteful to some. On the other hand, it should be generally gratifying that wave mechanics can be useful in describing and predicting mechanical behavior, even though the contemporary, orthodox view of wave mechanics is modified somewhat in the process. Indeed, the originators of the quantum theory were never quite satisfied with it. Only some of the second-generation disciples tend to accept contemporary wave mechanics with unquestioning devotion, convinced that all problems can be solved "in principle" by the proper use of the Schroedinger equation. In this book we are not satisfied with "in principle" solutions, but demonstrate how wave mechanics can, *in practice*, allow the calculation of macroscopic mechanical quantities such as transition velocities, non-elastic resonance frequencies, coefficients of sliding friction, and characteristic stresses. Some of the consequences of the modified wave-mechanical view range far outside the field of mechanical properties, and are mentioned only briefly. These include an improved explanation of particle diffraction by crystals, an interesting relation between lattice dissociation energy and a mean elastic sound velocity, and the concept of a particle-wave oscillator. Other areas of application of the new particle-wave view must eventually include fracture and fatigue, and time-dependent phenomena like creep, but these topics have not yet been fully treated in particle-wave terms. Nevertheless, the material presented in this book should be sufficient to demonstrate that the point of view presented is worth serious consideration.

The model of a crystal lattice used throughout is that of a regularly spaced array of point masses. This, at first, seems unrealistic since we are dealing with atom "diameters" of the order of 10^{-8} cm, and with interatomic distances of the same magnitude ($\sim 3 \times 10^{-8}$ cm). We are, however, concerned principally with linear momentum transfer between atoms. The *mass* of an atom is heavily concentrated in its nucleus, and nuclear diameters are of the order of 10^{-12} cm. Hence, linear momentum transfer between atoms will occur chiefly between nuclear masses with diameters about one-ten thousandth (or less) of the internuclear distances. In these terms, an array of point masses becomes a reasonable representation of the actual situation. It is interesting to speculate as to the possible role of angular momentum and angular momentum transfer in mechanical deformation, but this topic is not examined in the present book.

One of the most pleasant features of writing a book is the opportunity it presents for acknowledging the assistance and support received during the course of the work leading to the book. The measurements on mechanical resonance dispersion presented in Chapter II were carried out mainly in my laboratory at the Pennsylvania State University, and, since 1961, in my laboratory at the Johns Hopkins University, with the support of the Office of Naval Research (Acoustics Programs) and several grants from the National Science Foundation. I am much indebted to Professor James F. Bell for numerous discussions (and arguments!) concerning the facts of deformation revealed by both impact and stress–strain measurements. The numerous references to Professor Bell's work in Chapters III, IV, and VI attest to this more strikingly than anything I can say here. The experimental facts of hypervelocity impact were carefully laid out for me in numerous sessions with Professor Robert B. Pond, who also contributed to my stress–strain education and supplied data which is cited in Chapters III and IV. General discussions with Professors Robert E. Green, Jr. and Jerald L. Ericksen were helpful, and I wish to mention the assistance of Professor Clifford Truesdell who acted as my anagram man in connection with Chapter V.

Finally, particular thanks must go to Professor John A. Sauer of Rutgers University who read the draft manuscript and made numerout suggestions for changes. Professor Sauer's suggestions were adopted and have improved the book in all respects.

Baltimore
March 17, 1966   Edwin R. Fitzgerald

CONTENTS

PARTICLES, WAVES, AND MOMENTUM TRANSFER IN CRYSTALS

Introduction

My purpose here is to present a new view or theory of mechanical deformation in solids and not to discuss an old one. Before starting, however, it is appropriate to mention briefly the dislocation concepts in terms of which all current explanations of mechanical properties are couched. The idea of line imperfections or dislocations is an old one going back at least to Volterra[1] (1907) and then Love,[2] who treated both line and point defects as singularities in an elastic continuum. The suggestion that plastic deformation in crystals occurs through the motion of such dislocations was advanced separately by Taylor,[3] Orowan,[4] and Polyani[5] in 1934. The concept of screw dislocations was added to that of an edge dislocation in 1939 by Burgers,[6] who also applied the elastic theory of Volterra to calculate the stress field of a dislocation. A similar approach has been followed by a host of investigators since; that is, a calculation of the forces or interactions between dislocations and/or point defects is made in terms of a linear, isotropic, homogeneous, elastic continuum surrounding the imperfections. The results are then necessarily expressed in terms of an elastic modulus, G, and Poisson's ratio, or other pairs of elastic constants. A variation in the degree of sophistication may exist[7,8] in these "dislocation theories," but they all have one feature in common, viz., an attempt is made to describe a *non-elastic phenomenon* (plastic slip) entirely in terms of *linear elastic concepts*.

In my opinion, this is an illogical and ill-fated enterprise. After almost thirty years, this approach has led to no numerical calculation in agreement with measured values of any mechanical quantity— except through the arbitrary assignment of values to several "constants." A general stress-strain law in agreement with the experimental results has not been developed, even in *form*. Often, qualitative provisions for the very *existence* of certain well-known classes of mechanical behavior are missing. The occurrence of non-elastic audiofrequency modes, hypervelocity effects such as impact crater formation, and even the directional nature of slip are not adequately explained in these dislocation "theories." On the other hand, there can be little doubt that point and line imperfections are in some way associated with the plastic-deformation process. The *observations* of dislocations are numerous and the result of excellent experimental techniques. The only serious criticism on this score is that too few observations of moving slip lines or bands are available, but notable exceptions are the investigations of Pond and Harrison[9] and Hirsch.[10] In short, there *are* dislocations; fascinating pictures of them can be taken, and the resulting patterns are entertaining.

In looking for a new approach to describe non-elastic deformation in crystalline solids, it is natural to turn to wave mechanics. If one considers the various properties of solids now generally studied in connection with solid-state physics, it is clear that wave-mechanical concepts play a fundamental role in all areas save one—that of mechanical properties. Here alone the concepts remain classical. A crystal is considered to be equivalent to an array of quantized harmonic oscillators for thermodynamic properties (e.g., specific heat), but, evidently at the same time, the oscillators are classical for mechanical purposes. The electrical conduction of metals is described through quantum statistics and the Schroedinger equation, but metal plasticity remains classical—and unperturbed. We search in vain for Planck's constant in any of the interrelations between mechanical quantities, even when these are said to represent interactions on an atomic scale. If we find h at all, it is only as the symbol for sample thickness!

We must wonder, then, why there is this difference between the atomic interactions influencing mechanical properties and those leading to all other properties of solids. Is wave mechanics really not pertinent to mechanical deformation, or have we lacked the necessary cleverness to apply it? In the language of our epigraph, are mechanical phenomena all awry?

Did the Hand then of the Potter shake?

1. The Wave Character of Moving Particles

To answer the questions just posed, we turn first to the central fact of wave mechanics. That is, the evidence for the existence of certain waves or wavelike properties associated with moving particles. As first proposed by de Broglie[11] (1924), every particle of matter with momentum, P, has associated with it a certain "pilot" wave (or wave packet) of wavelength, λ, where

$$\lambda = \frac{h}{P} = \frac{h}{mv} \qquad (1.1)$$

when the momentum of a particle of mass, m, with velocity, v, is adequately described as $P = mv$ (i.e., for $v \ll$ speed of light, c). In his original arguments, de Broglie was influenced by the fact that the photoelectric effect had been explained by Einstein[12] in terms of certain particle-like properties associated with light waves. He concluded that particles might conversely have a wavelike character. de Broglie actually considered a time-dependent oscillation about a fixed point $x'y'z'$ in a given system of coordinates, and then showed that motion of the system with velocity, v, relative to a second system xyz resulted in an observer in the second frame seeing a running wave with wavelength $\lambda = h/P$, as in Eq. 1.2 below (for translational motion with the x axes of both systems remaining in coincidence).

$$\psi' = \psi'_0 \cos 2\pi\nu't'$$

$$\psi = \psi_0 \cos 2\pi \left(\nu t - \frac{x}{\lambda} \right) \qquad (1.2)$$

It is important to emphasize that the exact nature of the stationary oscillations, ψ', or the running wave, ψ, associated with the particle were not specified by de Broglie. He first speculated that each individual particle was connected with a system of "pilot" waves, so that the path of the particle coincided with the ray of the wave system. Then, as it did not seem reasonable to connect an extended wave with a single, localized particle, he proposed that a narrow wave packet or pulse would be more appropriate. Such a packet can be shown to result from the superposition of a group of waves, each of infinite extent in space, but of slightly different frequencies. As long as each component wave of the group propagates with the same *phase* velocity, the packet will hang together and keep its original shape, but for differing phase velocities the packet will spread with time. The velocity of the packet is given by the group velocity

$$v_g = \partial\nu/\partial(1/\lambda) \qquad (1.3)$$

and it is very easily demonstrated that this velocity is the particle velocity of a free particle generating the wave ($v_g = v$).

The most direct experimental confirmations of the existence of these particle waves are the various diffraction experiments which have been carried out with beams of electrons, neutrons, and various atoms and molecules by Davisson and Germer,[13] Thompson,[14] Rupp,[15] Worsnop,[16] Zinn,[17] Estermann and Stern,[18] Johnson,[19] Ellet, Olson, and Zahl,[20] and many others. In all of these experiments, a narrow *external* beam of particles of nearly equal velocities is directed toward the surface of a crystal (or ruled grating) and the space distribution of the density of scattered particles is observed by a suitable detector.

The general result is that regions of high and low density of scattered particles are observed, corresponding to the interference properties expected of waves. The angular density patterns obtained are usually explained in terms of the two-dimensional (surface) grating formula

$$n\lambda = D \sin \theta \qquad (1.4)$$

or the three-dimensional (space) grating relation

$$n\lambda = 2\boldsymbol{d} \sin \theta \qquad (1.5)$$

where D and $\boldsymbol{d}$ are characteristic spacings of the crystal used, n is an integer, and θ is the angular displacement in the plane of the beam and the surface normal.

High-speed electrons also show diffraction in transmission through thin single-crystal films, as first shown by Kikuchi[21] in mica, and through thin polycrystalline films, as demonstrated by Thompson[14] (1928) for gold, platinum, and aluminum. Diffraction of electrons from a ruled optical grating has been reported by Rupp,[15] and an indication of diffraction of hydrogen from a ruled metal grating was obtained by Knauer and Stern.[22] Atomic and molecular particles successfully used in surface diffraction experiments have included, H, He, H_2, As_4, Cd, Zn, Hg, and Ag.

In spite of the strong experimental evidence for the existence of some type of wavelike properties associated with particles, it does not follow that all is understood in this connection. In the original and justly famous Davisson and Germer experiment,[13] for example, beams of low-voltage electrons (25–370 volts) were normally incident on the

(111) face of a nickel single crystal. Thirty sets of elastically scattered or diffracted beams (no energy loss) were observed; of these, just three confirmed the de Broglie relation (1–2%) in the surface grating formula; six sets of beams were attributed to the surface structure of absorbed gas on the nickel; one set was unexplained; and 20 sets seemed to correspond to the space-grating formula, but showed systematic deviations. These 20 sets with systematic deviations were later "fixed up" (i.e., brought into agreement) by considering the electrons inside the crystal to have a different wavelength, λ', as a result of a mean "inner potential," V_i, in the crystal. In general, it has subsequently been found that, by a suitable choice of inner potential, such results can always be brought into agreement with the space-grating equation for a certain range of wavelengths. Thus Farnsworth[23] determined the inner potential of copper, gold, and silver single crystals; wide variations were found, depending on the angle of incidence of the bombarding electron beam. In zinc single crystals, Kalashinkov and Yakolev[24] found variations in inner potential from 10 to 27 electron volts as the order of diffraction increased, and also noted some unexplained beams. In recent work, Germer and associates[25] report a number of unexplained results in diffraction from the (110) face of a nickel single crystal, including a "surprising" penetration of a normally incident 13-volt beam.

In atomic beam and molecular beam experiments, positive results were obtained only for *some* atoms and molecules diffracted from *some* crystals acting as two-dimensional surface gratings. Thus H, H_2, and He were successfully diffracted (for certain directions of incidence) from NaCl and LiF crystals, but no diffraction was observed from a number of other crystals tried by Estermann and Stern.[18] Ellet, Olson, and Zahl[20] successfully diffracted mercury (Hg), cadmium (Cd), and arsenic (As_4) from NaCl crystals, but Ellet and Olson[26] found no diffraction of sodium atoms from NaCl. Taylor[27] also reported negative results for lithium, potassium, and cesium beams against crystals of NaCl or LiF. A strange result, discussed by Zahl,[28] was the evidence for considerable penetration (space-grating effects) for both zinc and cadmium atom beams against sodium chloride.

Hence, it is fair to state that, in spite of very strong and numerous experimental confirmations of diffraction effects associated with particle beams, a few mysteries still remain.

2. The Contemporary View of Wave Mechanics—
Probability Waves

Within a few years of de Broglie's first paper, Schroedinger[29] proposed a differential wave equation for the associated matter wave, ψ, and Born[30] suggested that $|\psi|^2$ could be thought of as a probability function which, for a single particle, gives the probability of finding it in various positions in space. Schroedinger arrived at his equation partly by analogy with the wave equations for sound and light waves, starting with the corresponding expression for a plane wave of the unspecified wave property, ψ, of the particle,

$$\psi = \psi_0 e^{-i2\pi(\nu t - x/\lambda)} \tag{1.6}$$

Upon substituting for ν and λ in terms of the quantum energy relation and the de Broglie relation, viz.,

$$\nu = E/h \qquad \lambda = \frac{h}{P}$$

and differentiating the resulting equations with respect to time and x, he noticed that

$$\psi = \psi_0 e^{-(i/\hbar)(E t - Px)}$$

$$\frac{\partial \psi}{\partial t} = -\frac{i}{\hbar} E\psi$$

$$\frac{\partial^2 \psi}{\partial x^2} = -\left(\frac{P}{\hbar}\right)^2 \psi \tag{1.7}$$

where $\hbar = h/2\pi$.

Since the total energy, E, of the particle with mass m can be written as the sum of kinetic and potential energies

$$E = \frac{P^2}{2m} + V \tag{1.8}$$

it was apparent that the following combination of Eqs. 1.7 and 1.8 was identically zero:

$$\frac{\partial^2 \psi}{\partial x^2} - \frac{2m}{\hbar^2} V\psi + \frac{2im}{\hbar} \frac{\partial \psi}{\partial t} = 0 \tag{1.9}$$

(Schroedinger equation in one dimension)

In three dimensions a corresponding result is obtained as shown below.

$$\nabla^2\psi - \frac{2m}{\hbar^2} V\psi + \frac{2im}{\hbar} \frac{\partial\psi}{\partial t} = 0 \tag{1.10}$$

(Schroedinger equation in three dimensions)

Of course, it is possible after the fact to devise much more elegant means of obtaining Eq. 1.10 by using "operators" or devising new systems of mathematical mechanics. These methods have a certain neatness and appeal, but cannot remove the arbitrary assumptions inherent in the equation. Instead, other sets of arbitrary assumptions are taken on which serve only to disguise the situation. Thus, the Schroedinger equation is a postulate to which are often added the further requirements that physically acceptable solutions must be single valued and continuous, if a probability interpretation is to be given to $|\psi|^2$. The role of the Schroedinger equation as a certain type of "primary assumption" has been nicely discussed by Pauling and Wilson.[31] The validity (or perhaps usefulness) of such an assumption is demonstrated by its successful application in both explaining and predicting experimental results. One of the most gratifying things about the Schroedinger equation, therefore, is that it shows, in a very clear way, how the imposition of boundary conditions or force fields on a particle leads to discrete energy states for the particle and to quantized momentum values. In the same year that he proposed the equation, Schroedinger[29] applied it to the hydrogen atom, the harmonic oscillator, the rigid rotator, the diatomic molecule, and the hydrogen atom in an electric field. Other applications have been numerous, and the success of this approach has been great, if not quite complete. Solutions to the equation are not confined to plane waves; a combination of waves forming a packet is also a solution. In certain cases a solution can be found which is a product of a function of position alone and a function of time alone

$$\psi(x,y,z,t) = \psi_0(x,y,z)\, e^{-iEt/\hbar} \tag{1.11}$$

where $\psi_0(xyz)$ satisfies the standing wave equation

$$\nabla^2\psi_0 + \frac{2m}{\hbar^2} (E - V)\, \psi_0 = 0 \tag{1.12}$$

The types of potential functions V for which *exact* solutions of this time-independent equation have been found are quite limited even for a single particle. Furthermore, exact solutions for the wave functions of two or more particles are difficult, if not impossible, for almost any type of potential function. Instead, approximations or perturbations are used; these have been surprisingly successful in explaining qualitatively certain experimental results. In speaking of two particles, we ought to mention the Schroedinger equation for this case,

$$\nabla_1^2\psi + \nabla_2^2\psi - \frac{2m}{\hbar^2}(V_1 + V_2 + V_{12})\,\psi + \frac{2im}{\hbar}\frac{\partial\psi}{\partial t} = 0 \qquad (1.13)$$

an equation which can be easily obtained through the use of the operators mentioned before. Here, the subscripts 1 and 2 refer to the sets of coordinates $(x_1y_1z_1)$ and $(x_2y_2z_2)$; V_1, V_2 are the potential energies of particles 1 and 2 in whatever field is present, and V_{12} is a possible interaction potential. From Eq. 1.13, one can (by extrapolation) readily imagine the practical difficulty in obtaining exact solutions or even good approximations for the corresponding equations of 3, 4, 6, 10, or 100 or more particles. Yet, if this method is to be used to describe macroscopic properties of crystals, the number of particles involved will be of the order of 10^{23}, even for very small samples.

In addition to the scarcity of exact solutions for ψ, the meaning to be attached to ψ when it is known has been the source of considerable discussion. In fact, in the contemporary view, a meaning is attached only to $|\psi|^2$, not to ψ itself. Thus, for a single particle, the probability of finding the particle at a particular position (xyz) at a given time is proportional to $|\psi|^2$; where $|\psi|^2$ is high, the chances of observing the particle are good, (i.e., the probability density is high), but there always exists the possiblity of finding it somewhere else. The wave function for two particles is similarly used to obtain a probability density, $|\psi(1,2)|^2$, for simultaneously observing particle 1 in position $(x_1y_1z_1)$ and particle 2 in position $(x_2y_2z_2)$. From this, we see that the probability-wave function for two particles must depend on six coordinates, and this alone indicates that it is difficult to attach any ordinary meaning to the wave function in this case.

In spite of the practical and conceptual difficulties connected with the application of the Schroedinger-Born probability-wave view of particle waves, it is now widely accepted.

One of the most ingenious applications of contemporary probability-wave mechanics has been the rationalization of particle-wave diffraction. The occurrence of such diffraction is the strongest and most direct evidence for the existence of some wavelike properties of particles, but, as we have seen, the only waves supposed to be associated with the particle are the completely nonphysical probability waves. To account for the diffraction of particles by crystals in these terms, the following argument is advanced: Associated with each incident particle of a certain velocity, v_i, is a probability wave packet $\psi(x,y,z,t)$ with the property that the probability of observing the particle within any little volume of space, $dx\, dy\, dz$ is

$$p = |\psi|^2\, dx\, dy\, dz \qquad (1.14)$$

and all incident particles in a homogeneous velocity beam have the same form of packet, ψ. In striking the crystal, each particle "interacts" in such a way that its probability wave packet changes to a new function, $\psi'(x,y,z,t)$, which again is the same for each particle. This new function must have certain maxima and minima, as a function of its space coordinates, in order to account for the observed diffraction effects, as indicated schematically in Figure 1.1. For a thin polycrystalline film, the observed pattern is a central spot and a series of concentric rings. Since these rings are found to be farther apart as the detecting screen is moved away from the film along the x axis, it follows that the diffracted wave packet must spread in the yz directions as the packet advances. The probability distributions do not imply that single particles break up as a result of diffraction and appear simultaneously at various points on a detecting screen. Instead, the probability patterns merely indicate the most likely (and unlikely) positions at which each particle may be observed. Each particle transmitted will be observed at only *one* position on the screen, but exactly where cannot be predicted in advance. Only if several thousand single particles are consecutively sent through the film can we predict that most of them will be found at the center, the next greatest number at the position of the second maximum ring, etc. According to the orthodox view,[32] the act of observing an individual particle collapses the wave packet and forces the position of the particle to be sharp (at the same time, the uncertainty in its momentum increases). This collapse, in the final analysis, must result from the interaction of the particle with the screen.

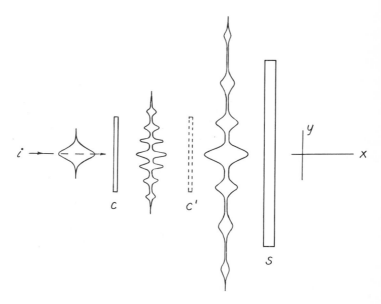

Fig. 1.1. Diagram showing y-dependence of a central cross section of the probability function $\psi(x,y,z)$ which must be associated with a particle, such as an electron in transmission diffraction through a thin polycrystalline film, C. The original wave packet (to the left of C) must be transformed into a probability-wave function with multiple maxima (shown to the right of C), as a result of the diffraction process. The observed pattern on the detecting screen, S, is a central spot and concentric rings after many electrons have passed through C. Since the pattern spreads as the distance between C and S increases, the probability-wave function must also spread as indicated.

Here we have a remarkable property of matter; in one case, particle interaction with the condensed matter of the polycrystalline film produces a *spread* of the packet, but in the next instance, interaction with the screen results in a *contraction* of the wave packet! If a second polycrystalline film is now inserted between the screen and the first crystal, as indicated by the dashed lines in Figure 1.1, we can ask what happens to the wave packet spread by the first film when it strikes the second? The only answer can be that, as a particle, it must "strike" or interact with the second film at only one spot; thus the wave packet is collapsed as it enters, but spread as it leaves the second film, since a diffraction pattern is still observed on the screen. Next, imagine a series of polycrystalline films to be successively thinner and closer together, until the case is approached where there are rows of atoms 10^{-8} cm apart. As the incident probability-wave packet interacts with the first atomic plane, it collapses, then spreads, then collapses on reaching the second plane, only to spread as it leaves, and so on, until the packet fights its way clear to the back surface and a final spread to allow for the observed diffraction pattern!

Without going into further detail, we merely suggest that there is perhaps one question in wave mechanics that has not been answered fully by the probability-wave view of particle waves.

That question is: *Why are particles diffracted like waves in interactions with crystals?*

3. AN ALTERNATIVE TO THE SCHROEDINGER EQUATION

In the preceding brief discussion of contemporary wave mechanics, it has been hinted that our present understanding of the wave/particle aspect of matter might still be improved. Various deficiencies and paradoxes associated with the orthodox (probability) view of wave mechanics have been pointed out by Einstein,[33] Planck,[34] Schroedinger,[35] Renninger,[36] and, within the last few years, de Broglie.[37] In addition, prosaic objections may be raised. While in principle we know everything from the Schroedinger equation, in practice we know chiefly the hydrogen atom. Furthermore, it seems likely that a description of macroscopic mechanical properties in terms of solutions to the appropriate Schroedinger equation, even if feasible (with computers), would be extremely unwieldy because of the large number of constants required.

Thus we assert that if the correct Schroedinger equation is written for a macroscopic crystal sample (i.e., for 10^{23} particles) an *exact* solution cannot be found; if found, such a solution cannot be understood. It is still possible, of course, that an approximation involving the Schroedinger equation might give fairly good results, as in the case of band theory, where the interaction of an electron with the crystal lattice is expressed in terms of a periodic potential. However, such an approximation has not been found, and therefore it seems likely that the path to a wave-mechanical description of macroscopic mechanical properties is not through use of the Schroedinger equation; instead, a new approach must be tried.

Our first suggestion is that there are, after all, *two* kinds of waves associated with particles. There are indeed the Schroedinger-Born probability waves; these are invaluable in many instances, and there is no thought of discarding them. These probability waves, in fact, can be associated with *all* types of particles; light particles (photons), sound particles (phonons), and matter particles (atoms, electrons, etc.) all have appropriate probability wave packets. We notice that phonons and photons each have momentum, which is all that is required by the de Broglie relation to generate the probability wave; that is, no *rest* mass is necessary.

For all particles, we expect associated probability waves, ψ, which can be obtained from Schroedinger or Dirac-type equations. *We also expect that there will be some real-property wave* associated with each of these particles. In the cases of the photon and phonon, these real property waves are known to be electromagnetic waves and sound waves, respectively. A real physical property is propagated by the electromagnetic wave associated with the photon, that is, an electric field. A real physical property is also propagated by the sound wave associated with a phonon, viz., displacement. In connection with the propagation of these physical properties, the relevant wave functions are not solutions of a Schroedinger probability-wave equation, but are instead solutions of certain different sets of equations. These equations, of course, are Maxwell's equations and the ordinary wave equation for elastic displacement in a material medium.

Now the question naturally arises—what are the missing real-property and differential wave equations for matter waves? If found, these are apt to be of much more use in connection with macroscopic mechanical properties of large assemblies of particles than are the probability waves. A natural choice for the real physical property is momentum, since the de Broglie relation itself contains that property. We can hope to find the proper differential equation partly by analogy and partly by luck; then, as in the case of the Schroedinger equation, the correctness of these ideas can be tested only by their success in describing and predicting experimental results.

4. Internal Generation of Particle Waves in Crystals

So far, no specific union between particle waves and deformation has been described. Indeed, at first, these must appear to be two unrelated subjects, but, as implied by our title, we expect to couple them, It is this connection, in fact, which leads to a differential equation for particle momentum waves, and the idea for the connection is a very simple one. There is ample evidence that *external* beams of particles (including atoms and molecules) behave like waves in their interactions with crystals; therefore, it can be expected that *internal* beams or even single particles in a crystal will evidence wavelike properties. Further, it may be possible that, under mechanical load, some of the atoms in a crystal move through sections of the crystal lattice as waves rather than as classical particles. Hence, one can imagine that, after large numbers of atoms (moving consecutively or simultaneously) have moved through the crystal, a total macroscopic deformation will be evident as a consequence of these wave motions. In order to make these ideas more specific, Figure 1.2 may now be considered.

Here (Fig. 1.2a), an external field-free atom of mass m and with velocity, v_0, is pictured as incident on a crystal surface. This particle may be only one of a beam, but the experimental evidence already cited convinces us that it will interact as a wave with at least the surface atoms of the crystal. Now we turn to the situation shown in Figure 1.2b, where an atom *within* the crystal occupies a narrow field-free region, such as the interlattice position indicated. If this particular atom attains a velocity, v_i, within the field-free region (through loading, as will be discussed shortly), we can again expect it to interact with, or perhaps even propagate through, the lattice as a wave with wavelength $\lambda = h/mv_i$. In proposing such an *internally generated* particle wave as a mechanism for non-elastic deformation, it is clear that a considerable "range" or depth of penetration will have to exist if large deformations are to occur by this process. Such an extended range does not at first seem in accord with the facts of *external* atomic diffraction, where mostly surface effects are found, but there is the possibility that surface barriers hinder external penetration, and these will be absent for internal field-free atoms. Further, we note that the velocities of the atoms and molecules used in diffraction experiments were all in a narrow range between about 0.5×10^4 and 5×10^5 cm/sec; there is a chance that this may be a stopping band. Then, field-free particles of *lower* velocity might actually penetrate more deeply into crystals than do high-velocity particles. To support this possibility, we recall the surprising penetration of zinc and cadmium

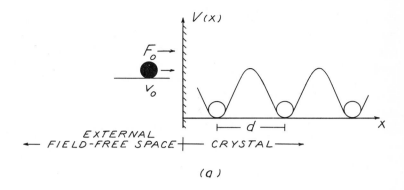

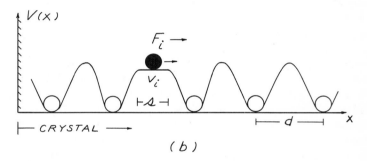

Fig. 1.2. (a) Schematic representation of an external field-free atom incident with velocity, v_0, on a crystal with periodic potential variation, $V(x)$,
in a lattice of spacing, **d**. (b) Representation of an internal field-free atom
with incident velocity, v_i, in a crystal with periodic potential and spacing, **d**.
The width of the internal field-free region is $s = pd$ (where $p < 1$), as
indicated.

atoms into sodium chloride reported by Zahl[28]—a result which has
also been discussed by Fraser.[38]

The opportunity for the presence of field-free atoms in a real
crystal is present without question. There is overwhelming experimental evidence for the existence of various crystal defects. The
atoms in the half-plane of an edge dislocation are in field-free interlattice regions, as may be individual interlattice atoms, atoms near
vacancies, etc. The field-free regions may be very narrow and not
necessarily symmetrically disposed around the atoms in question,
leading to orientation effects. Now the idea that the movement of

sheets of atoms, like those forming an edge dislocation, produces plastic deformation is precisely the accepted concept of dislocation motion. However, we propose to treat this motion quite differently, as summarized below.

Particle-Wave View of Non-Elastic Motion

(1) The macroscopic deformation of a crystalline solid is the collective result of the individual motions of certain internal field-free atoms in the solid.

(2) These atoms proceed through the crystal *as particle momentum waves*, and not under the action of, or governed exclusively by, elastic forces or properties of the material.

(3) The wavelength associated with the deformation may be calculated from the final velocity, v_i, acquired by these internal atoms just before they leave the initially field-free regions where their motion starts, according to the de Broglie relation, i.e., by $\lambda = h/mv_i$.

In addition to these basic concepts, there must be some provision for the influence of an external, mechanical load on the particle wave propagation. This follows from the self-evident connection between load and deformation. The role of external stress in particle-wave deformation will be treated more extensively later, but can be quickly sketched here. Imagine a certain average force per unit area (or stress), Y_0, present in each cross section of a crystal block and in a direction where the crystal spacing is d. If we now let ζ be the number of atoms per cross-sectional area, then the average force, F_i, on each atom in such a plane will be

$$F_i = Y_0/\zeta \tag{1.15}$$

An atom located in a field-free region of width pd in the direction of the force will then be accelerated until it reaches the end of the field-free region; after this, it propagates through the crystal with a wavelength determined by the final velocity, v_i, attained in its initial particle motion. To find the velocity, we equate the work done by the force F_i through the distance pd to the final kinetic energy of the particle.

$$F_i\,pd = \frac{1}{2}\,mv_i^2 \tag{1.16}$$

or

$$v_i = \sqrt{\frac{2F_i\,pd}{m}}$$

and hence, from the de Broglie relation and Eq. 1.15, it follows that

$$\lambda = h \sqrt{\frac{\zeta}{2pm\boldsymbol{d}Y_0}} \tag{1.17}$$

providing the required relation between external stress and the particle-wave aspect of deformation. We shall have more to say about this equation and the field-free parameter, p, later.

Since the process of plastic deformation is often associated with translational slip, we may loosely refer to these internally generated particle momentum waves as "slip waves."

5. Particle Waves in an Infinite One-Dimensional Lattice

Before considering wave motion in a periodic lattice of point masses, a specific statement or definition of wave motion in such a discontinuous medium is in order. Consider a general nth mass in a row lattice, as depicted in Figure 1.3. Let ψ_n be some measurable property of the nth lattice mass (atom) which can be defined in the vicinity of the mass site, but not elsewhere. Then ψ_n is said to be propagated as a wave if a differential equation for ψ_n can be set up (on a physical basis) with a solution of the form

$$\psi_n = A e^{-i(2\pi\nu t - kn\boldsymbol{d})} \tag{1.18}$$

where $k = 2\pi/\lambda$ is the wave vector, $\boldsymbol{d}$ is the lattice spacing, ν is frequency, and $n\boldsymbol{d}$ is the equilibrium position of mass n relative to the

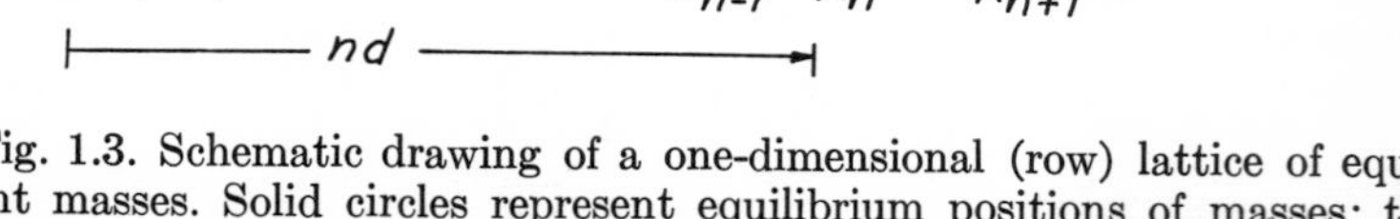

Fig. 1.3. Schematic drawing of a one-dimensional (row) lattice of equal point masses. Solid circles represent equilibrium positions of masses; the dashed circles represent the positions of deflected or displaced masses (atoms).

origin. A common case is that of an elastic displacement wave, where the relevant property, ψ_n, is the longitudinal or transverse displacement from equilibrium (x_n or y_n). For an elastic interaction, K_e, between such masses, the well-known differential equation for displacement of the nth mass (for nearest-neighbor interaction only) is given by:

$$m \frac{\partial^2 x_n}{\partial t^2} = -K_e(x_n - x_{n-1}) - K_e(x_n - x_{n+1})$$

$$= K_e(x_{n+1} + x_{n-1} - 2x_n) \tag{1.19}$$

with a solution

$$x_n(t) = A e^{-i(2\pi\nu_e t - knd)} \tag{1.20}$$

where the frequency, ν_e, must be given by

$$\nu_e = \frac{1}{\pi} \sqrt{\frac{K_e}{m}} \sin \frac{kd}{2} \tag{1.21}$$

in order for Eq. 1.20 to be a solution of Eq. 1.19. From Eq. 1.21, it follows that there is a limiting or cutoff frequency, $\nu_m = \sqrt{K_e}/\pi\sqrt{m}$, above which elastic waves will not propagate through the lattice.

(a) Differential Equation for Momentum Transfer

If momentum is now considered as the property to be propagated along the lattice, we can imagine that there might be an interaction between masses which depends on the relative *velocities* of the masses (instead of relative displacements). By analogy with the case for elastic displacement waves, we suppose the lattice to be characterized by a *velocity* interaction constant, $\mathbf{K}_p$, such that a differential equation for the velocity of the nth mass is

$$m \frac{\partial v_n}{\partial t} = \mathbf{K}_p(v_{n+1} + v_{n-1} - 2v_n) \tag{1.22}$$

The physical basis for Eq. 1.22 can be strengthened by a slight rearrangement as shown below:

$$\frac{\partial(mv_n)}{\partial t} = \mathbf{K}_p(v_{n-1} - v_n) - \mathbf{K}_p(v_n - v_{n+1}) \tag{1.23}$$

where, for a particle wave traveling from left to right, we note that

$\dfrac{\partial (mv_n)}{\partial t}$ represents the net time rate of change of momentum at lattice point n

$\mathbf{K}_p(v_{n-1} - v_n)$ is the rate of momentum transfer from point $n - 1$ to point n

$\mathbf{K}_p(v_n - v_{n+1})$ is the rate of momentum transfer from point n to point $n + 1$

$\mathbf{K}_p$ is the *momentum transfer constant* of the lattice for a particle wave.

Equations 1.22 and 1.23 then are simply statments of conservation of momentum between the three interacting particles. It can be shown that a solution to Eq. 1.22 is of the form (cf. Appendix A):

$$v_n = Be^{-i(2\pi v_p t - knd)} \tag{1.24}$$

where the frequency, v_p, is now specified by

$$v_p = -i\,\frac{2\mathbf{K}_p}{\pi m} \sin^2 \frac{k d}{2} \tag{1.25}$$

In order for v_p to be real and positive, $\mathbf{K}_p$ must be imaginary, such that

$$\mathbf{K}_p = iK_p \tag{1.26}$$

and then

$$v_p = \frac{2K_p}{\pi m} \sin^2 \frac{k d}{2} \tag{1.27}$$

so that a limiting frequency, $v'_m = 2K_p/\pi m$, occurs for particle momentum wave propagation through the lattice.

The occurrence of i in the momentum transfer constant indicates that the rate of momentum transfer is out of phase with the velocities of the masses and, in fact, must lag the velocity of the nth mass by 90°. The units of $\mathbf{K}_p$ are those of a mechanical impedance (force/velocity) and hence, we expect that, in general, it may be complex for oscillating velocities and forces such as those involved in particle-wave propagation. The occurrence of i in this quantity, therefore, presents no cause for alarm.

(b) The Momentum Transfer Constant

In the choice of a differential equation for particle-momentum wave propagation in a periodic lattice, a momentum transfer constant of magnitude, K_p, was used to specify some type of velocity interaction or momentum transfer factor. We next turn to a closer examination of K_p, and attempt to find a value for it. To do this, we notice that, for very long wavelengths of a particle wave (low values of k), the closely spaced periodic variation of potential in the lattice cannot have any effect on the wave. To put it another way, the lattice acts as a field-free region to long wavelengths where

$$\lambda_p \gg d \tag{1.28}$$

Therefore, we expect that, in the limit as $k \to 0$, the expression for ν_p of a particle wave in a lattice (Eq. 1.27) must reduce to that for a free particle:

$$\frac{2K_p}{\pi m} \sin^2 \frac{kd}{2} = \frac{\hbar}{4\pi m} k^2 \qquad (k \to 0) \tag{1.29}$$

where $\hbar k^2 / 4\pi m$ is the free-particle frequency. But at small values of k (and hence $kd/2$), we replace the sine by its argument, and therefore:

$$\frac{2K_p}{\pi m} \frac{k^2 d^2}{4} = \frac{\hbar}{4\pi m} k^2 \tag{1.30}$$

or

$$K_p = \hbar / 2d^2 \tag{1.31}$$

Hence, a value for K_p is determined by the physical boundary condition, on the particle wave in a lattice that at long wavelengths (small k) the variation of ν_p with k must be the same as that for a free particle. Since d is often of the order of 3.0×10^{-8} cm in crystals, an approximate value of K_p is 0.55×10^{-12} dyne-sec/cm.

We are not surprised to find that the momentum transfer constant involves Planck's constant; it will continue to appear in all our subsequent descriptions of deformation.

(c) Comparison of Elastic and Particle Waves—Limiting Velocities

It is instructive to compare various features of the ν vs. k curves for elastic and particle waves in a lattice, as indicated in Figure 1.4.

The corresponding ν–k curves for a continuous medium are shown by
the dashed lines in each case. These are obtained on the basis of the
one-dimensional lattice, by letting the spacing, d, approach zero, so
that $d \ll \lambda$ for all values of k. A continuous one-dimensional medium

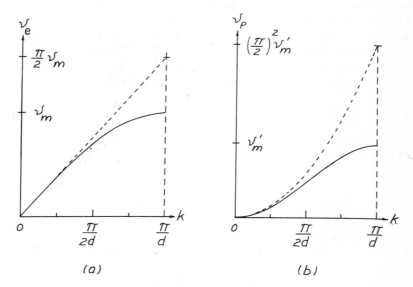

Fig. 1.4. (a) Frequency vs. wave vector, k, for an elastic displacement
wave (solid line) in an infinite row lattice of spacing, d, compared with the
frequency-wave vector characteristic for a continuous medium (dashed line)
formed by letting $d \to 0$. (b) Frequency vs. wave vector, k, for a particle-
momentum wave (solid line) in an infinite row lattice of spacing, d compared
with the frequency-wave vector characteristic for a continuous, field-free
medium (dashed line) by letting $d \to 0$.

formed in this way will also be field-free, since the equipotential
lattice sites become contiguous as $d \to 0$. The general equations for
ν_e and ν_p should reduce to the corresponding expressions for elastic
waves in a continuous string, and for free-particle waves, respectively.
This is actually the case for

$$\nu_e = \frac{1}{\pi} \sqrt{\frac{K_e}{m}} \, \frac{kd}{2} = \frac{1}{2\pi} \sqrt{\frac{K_e d}{m/d}} \, k \qquad (d \to 0)$$

where $K_e d$ is identified as the tension, and m/d is the mass per unit length. Similarly, we find

$$\nu_p = \frac{\hbar}{\pi m d^2} \frac{k^2 d^2}{4} = \frac{\hbar}{4\pi m} k^2 \qquad (d \to 0)$$

The ratio $2\pi\nu/k$ represents the phase velocity in each case, so that these quantities can be written as

$$c_{s\lambda}(\text{elastic}) = c_{s\infty} \left[\sin\left(\frac{kd}{2}\right) \middle/ \left(\frac{kd}{2}\right) \right] \qquad (1.32)$$

$$c_{p\lambda}(\text{particle}) = \frac{h}{2m\lambda} \left[\sin^2\left(\frac{kd}{2}\right) \middle/ \left(\frac{kd}{2}\right)^2 \right] \qquad (1.33)$$

From Eqs. 1.32 and 1.33, it follows that, at $\lambda = 2d$, the phase velocity for an elastic wave in the lattice is $(2/\pi)$ times the corresponding value for a continuous medium ($c_{s\infty}$), and, at this wavelength the same ratio is $(2/\pi)^2$ for a particle wave.

The group velocity of the waves is also of interest, since this velocity determines the rate of energy transfer in the lattice, and is the velocity of the probability wave packet for particle waves. This velocity is given by $2\pi(\partial\nu/\partial k)$ and, hence, is proportional to the slopes or tangents of the ν vs. k curves. Analytic expressions for the group velocities can be found by differentiating,

$$2\pi \frac{\partial\nu_e}{\partial k} = v_g(\text{elastic}) = d \sqrt{\frac{K_e}{m}} \cos\frac{kd}{2} \qquad (1.34)$$

$$2\pi \frac{\partial\nu_p}{\partial k} = v_g(\text{particle}) = \frac{h}{\pi m d} \sin\frac{kd}{2} \cos\frac{kd}{2} \qquad (1.35)$$

A comparison of the wave vector dependence of phase and group velocities, for elastic and particle waves, is presented in Figures 1.5 and 1.6, respectively. Both elastic and particle waves have zero group velocity at $\lambda = 2d$ (where $k = \pi/d$), which is equivalent to a standing wave with zero net energy transfer through the lattice. On the other hand, the group velocity of the elastic wave has its maximum at long wavelengths ($k = 0$), while the particle-wave maximum occurs at

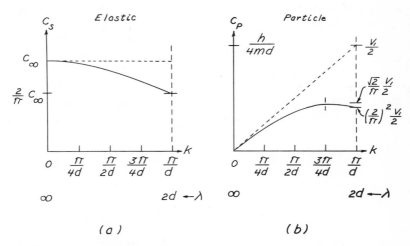

Fig. 1.5. (a) Variation of phase velocity with wave vector, k, for elastic waves in an infinite row lattice of spacing, d, and point masses, m (solid line), and in a continuum (dashed line). (b) Variation of phase velocity with wave vector, k, for particle waves in an infinite row lattice of spacing, d, and point masses, m (solid line), and in a field-free continuum (dashed line) where $v_1 = h/2md$.

$\lambda = 4\underline{d}$ (where $k = \pi/2d$). At long wavelengths, in fact, particle waves do not transmit energy in the lattice. This is not surprising, since the particle velocity for $\lambda \to \infty$ is zero according to the de Broglie relation.

The frequency dependence on wave vector is periodic for both elastic-displacement waves and particle-momentum waves. Cutoff frequencies, ν_m and ν'_m, respectively, appear, and these occur at $\lambda = 2d$, $2d/3$, $2d/5$, etc., so that a question arises as to the reason for such uncertainty in λ for a given value of ν. We can agree (by unanimous consent) to consider the frequency functions only in the interval $-\pi/d \le k \le \pi/d$, since all possible values of frequency occur in this range, and this will restrict values of λ to $\lambda \ge 2d$. This merely removes the ambiguity by convention, however, without saying anything of physical significance. The situation is really this: the displacement, x_n, for example, can only be measured at the position of the nth mass in the lattice, and we can expect to know nothing of displacement wave properties $between$ lattice masses. Suppose a set of displacements, x_i, are observed, as shown in Figure 1.7.

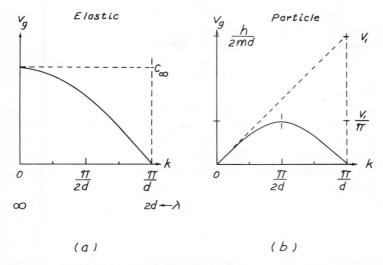

Fig. 1.6. (a) Variation of group velocity with wave vector, k, for elastic waves in an infinite row lattice of spacing d and point masses m (solid line), and in a continuum (dashed line). (b) Variation of group velocity with wave vector, k, for elastic waves in an infinite row lattice of spacing d and point masses m (solid line), and in a field-free continuum (dashed line) where $v_1 = h/2md$.

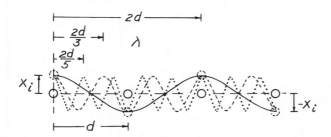

Fig. 1.7. Illustration of ambiguity in wavelength, λ, for observed displacements from equilibrium, $\pm x_i$, of masses in a row lattice of spacing, d, for wavelengths less than $2d$. Solid circles represent equilibrium positions of masses; dashed circles represent displaced positions at a particular time. These observed displacements could be attributed equally well to a wave of wavelength $\lambda = 2d$ (solid line), $\lambda = 2d/3$ (dashed line), or $\lambda = 2d/5$ (dotted line), etc., but real-property waves of the type defined in the text cannot exist for wavelengths less than $2d$.

These displacements may result from wave motion of length $2d$, as shown by the solid line; they may also be attributed to wave motion of length $2d/3$ (dashed line), $2d/5$ (dotted line), etc. Only if we could measure something between masses would the uncertainty illustrated be removed. Thus, at the very least, we can say that $\lambda = 2d$ is the smallest *measurable wavelength* that can exist in the lattice. Actually, we can say even more, viz., that real-property waves, ψ_n, of the type defined by Eq. 1.18 for a lattice, cannot exist in the lattice at wavelengths less than $2d$. Since the momentum of a mass, like its displacement, can only be defined in the vicinity of the mass, it follows that particle-momentum waves cannot propagate through the lattice with wavelengths less than $2d$. Then, from the de Broglie relation, there will be a limiting free-particle velocity, $v_p(\max)$, above which the associated particle wave will not propagate through the lattice, where

$$v_p(\max) = \frac{h}{2md} \qquad (1.36)$$

Some consequences of this velocity limit will become apparent in succeeding chapters, and will provide chances for experimental tests of these ideas.

6. Extension of the Results to Three-Dimensional Crystals

So far, particle-wave propagation has been considered only for an infinite one-dimensional lattice. We expect crystals to be neither infinite nor one-dimensional, and thus it seems like a good idea to consider what modifications are necessary to apply the results to real materials.

Consider first an infinitely large, three-dimensional, cubic lattice with spacing, d. It is again instructive to recall first the procedure used for elastic displacement waves in such a case. Elastic interactions between a general point mass (n,r,s) and *six* nearest neighbors as well as *twelve* next-nearest neighbors, have been taken into account for elastic waves. These calculations were first carried out by Born and von Karman[39] (1912, 1913) and have been clearly described by Smith.[40] The principal result of considering three dimensions is that differential equations for displacements in each of the x,y,z directions now appear, and coupling between displacements in different directions occurs. Thus, the differential equation for x displacement includes terms in x, in y, and in z, for example. Solutions are of the form:

$$x_{n,r,s} = Ae^{-i(2\pi \nu_e t - k_1 nd - k_2 rd - k_3 sd)}$$

$$y_{n,r,s} = Be^{-i(2\pi \nu_e t - k_1 nd - k_2 rd - k_3 sd)}$$

$$z_{n,r,s} = Ce^{-i(2\pi \nu_e t - k_1 nd - k_2 rd - k_3 sd)} \tag{1.37}$$

where the constants, A, B, and C are given in terms of three homogeneous equations involving the frequency and elastic interaction constants K_e, L_e, between nearest and next-nearest neighbors, respectively. The necessary condition for a solution to exist for this set of three equations is that a third-order determinant of the coefficients vanish. This condition leads to a cubic equation for ν_e^2 which can be solved for any particular direction (k_1, k_2, k_3) in k space, with the general result that three separate ν_e vs. k characteristics are found for a given direction. Of course, relative values of K_e and L_e are assumed; the calculations are usually only approximate, and in all cases are tedious. Other lattices which have been considered in this way are the body-centered cubic[41] and face-centered cubic.[42]

This approach can be applied to particle waves by considering momentum transfer or velocity interactions between a general point (n, r, s) and its nearest and next-nearest neighbors in a cubic lattice. Three differential equations for the velocities u, v, and w can be set up in terms of a nearest-neighbor momentum transfer constant, $\mathbf{K}_p$, and a next-nearest-neighbor momentum transfer constant $\mathbf{L}_p$. Since these equations represent statements of conservation of momentum in the three directions x, y, and z, however, they are uncoupled.

That is, momentum is independently conserved in each direction; the differential equation for the velocity, $v_{n,r,s}$, contains no terms in u or w, for example. This absence of coupling makes the solutions relatively simple, but again, these are of the form (cf. Appendix B),

$$u_{n,r,s} = De^{-i(2\pi \nu_p t - k_1 nd - k_2 rd - k_3 sd)}$$

$$v_{n,r,s} = Ee^{-i(2\pi \nu_p t - k_1 nd - k_2 rd - k_3 sd)}$$

$$w_{n,r,s} = Fe^{-i(2\pi \nu_p t - k_1 nd - k_2 rd - k_3 sd)} \tag{1.38}$$

and lead to *three* different ν_p vs. k characteristics for any general direction (k_1, k_2, k_3) in $\mathbf{k}$ space.

The occurrence of three ν–k curves for particle waves raises a fundamental difficulty not present for elastic waves. The connection between frequency and wavelength for elastic waves is through the phase velocity, c_s,

$$\nu_e = c_s/\lambda$$

and three possible values of frequency for the same wavelength can arise from different values of c_s, such as exist for transverse and longitudinal sound waves.

The existence of three different frequencies for the same wavelength of particle waves, however, implies that a free particle with one velocity can, in some manner, interact with the lattice in three different ways, and have three different energies ($h\nu_{pi}$) in the lattice. Yet this particle can have had only one energy while in its field-free position so long as we require adherence to the principle of

one mass, one velocity

The impossibility of the coexistence of three different particle-wave frequencies at one wavelength is also evident from a consideration of the situation at long wavelengths, where the lattice particle waves must behave like free-particle waves; three ν–k curves result in three values of group velocity, v_g, even at very small values of k, and thus require one mass to have three different particle velocities. It is also found that imposition of the necessary boundary condition, that the expressions for frequency as functions of wave vector reduce to the free-particle expression, leads to incompatible equations in this case (cf. Appendix B).

All these results demonstrate that the *differential equations selected to describe momentum transfer on the basis of multiple interactions in the lattice are physically incorrect descriptions of the process.*

Instead, we conclude that momentum transfer occurs from a lattice mass (atom) to only one other mass at a time. This is indicated schematically in Figure 1.8. Only in this way can a single ν vs. k curve be guaranteed. These three-dimensional considerations are described in more detail elsewhere,[43] but the practical outcome is that the results for a one-dimensional row lattice apply directly to three-dimensional lattices when the periodic spacing, d_j, between lattice masses in a

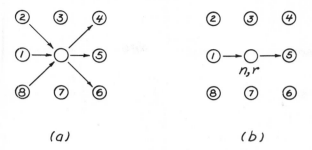

(a)   (b)

Fig. 1.8. Diagram depicting (a) multiple (simultaneous) momentum transfer from a single mass to three masses in a two-dimensional square lattice. In reality, the mass (n,r) can transfer momentum to only one mass at a time, as shown in (b). The assumption of simultaneous multiple momentum-transfer leads to both physical and mathematical contradictions, as discussed in the text.

particular direction, **k**, is used. It is easily shown, for example, that the momentum transfer constant in any direction with spacing $\boldsymbol{d}_j$ is

$$K_{pj} = \frac{\hbar}{2\boldsymbol{d}_j^2} \tag{1.39}$$

The momentum-transfer constant for any monatomic lattice will hence be largest in the direction of closest spacing, so that we expect slip to occur most readily in this direction. This is in accord with all experimental evidence.

Limiting velocities for the field-free particles generating particle-momentum waves can be calculated for any monatomic lattice in terms of the distance of closest approach, $\boldsymbol{d}_1$, by

$$v_1 = \frac{h}{2m\boldsymbol{d}_1} \tag{1.40}$$

and some representative values for cubic metals are listed in Tables 1.1 and 1.2.

The dual nature of matter is often mentioned as a very mysterious and complicated property of nature. In considering the propagation of particle momentum waves in periodic structures, however, this duality results in a very pleasing and simple result; that is, there is no essential difference between the results derived for one-, two-, or three-dimensional lattices.

TABLE 1.1

Limiting Velocities (v_1) for Some fcc Metals[a]

Metal	Atomic weight amu	d_1 <101> Å	λ_1 $2d_1$ Å	v_1 cm/sec
Al	26.98	2.86_2	5.72_4	$2.58_5 \times 10^3$
Ni	58.71	2.49_1	4.98_2	$1.36_4 \times 10^3$
Cu	63.54	2.55_6	5.11_2	$1.22_9 \times 10^3$
Pd	106.4	2.75_0	5.50_0	$.682_0 \times 10^3$
Ag	107.8	2.88_8	5.77_6	$.641_0 \times 10^3$
Pt	195.1	2.77_5	5.55_0	$.368_6 \times 10^3$
Au	197.0	2.88_4	5.76_8	$.351_2 \times 10^3$
Pb	207.2	3.49_9	6.99_8	$.275_3 \times 10^3$
Th	232.0	3.60	7.20	$.238_9 \times 10^3$

[a] Calculated from $v_1 = h/m\ \lambda_1$, where h is Planck's constant, $m =$ mass of metal atom, and $\lambda_1 = 2 \times$ atomic spacing in slip direction, d_1.

TABLE 1.2

Limiting Velocities (v_1) for Some bcc Metals[a]

Metal	Atomic weight amu	d_1 <111> Å	λ_1 $2d_1$ Å	v_1 cm/sec
Li	6.940	3.039	6.078	$9.46_2 \times 10^3$
Na	22.99	3.715	7.430	$2.33_6 \times 10^3$
K	39.10	4.627	9.254	$1.10_3 \times 10^3$
V	50.95	2.632	5.264	$1.48_8 \times 10^3$
Cr	52.01	2.498	4.996	$1.53_6 \times 10^3$
Fe	55.85	2.481	4.962	$1.44_0 \times 10^3$
Mo	95.95	2.725	5.450	$.763_1 \times 10^3$
W	183.86	2.739	5.478	$.396_2 \times 10^3$

[a] Calculated from $v_1 = h/m\lambda_1$ where h is Planck's constant, $m =$ mass of metal atom, and $\lambda_1 = 2 \times$ atomic spacing in slip direction, d_1.

Just as we cannot expect crystals to be one-dimensional, we do not count on them to be infinite. Quite apart from their overall finite dimensions, real crystals, because of defects, consist of small blocks or domains defining finite lattice segments of length S. It is well known that even single crystals have such a mosaic structure, although the misalignments between blocks may be very small in this case.

The presence of short lattice segments leads to the same form of ν vs. k curves as those for an infinite lattice, but now wave propagation occurs only for certain discrete values of the wave vector, k, given by

$$k = q\pi/N\boldsymbol{d}$$

$$q = 1, 2, 3, \ldots (N - 1)$$

where $S = N\boldsymbol{d}$ is the segment length. As a result, only certain discrete frequencies are propagated for both elastic and particle waves in a lattice. The occurrence of such particle-wave modes, and experimental evidence concerning them, will be described at length in the next chapter.

Conclusions

The point of view presented is quite different from usual ideas on deformation, so that a summary of the results so far may be in order:

(1) A wave equation for particle-momentum waves propagating in a periodic row-lattice has been set up in terms of velocity and a momentum transfer constant, $\mathbf{K}_p$. The physical basis for the equation is the principle of momentum conservation.

(2) A solution to the equation has been found giving a ν vs. k dependence. From this solution, expressions for the phase and group velocities were also obtained.

(3) The magnitude of the momentum transfer constant is $\hbar/2\boldsymbol{d}^2$, where $\boldsymbol{d}$ is the lattice spacing.

(4) It has been indicated that the one-dimensional results apply directly to three-dimensional lattices.

(5) A suggestion has also been made that there should be a characteristic velocity associated with plastic deformation in a crystal, dependent on the distance of closest approach, $\boldsymbol{d}_1$, and given by

$$v_1 = \frac{h}{2m\boldsymbol{d}_1}$$

These results relate Planck's constant to mechanical deformation, and will provide simple connections between deformation and other atomic and crystal constants.

In the following four chapters, these same ideas are used to describe the behavior of solids subject to dynamic loading, such as vibration and high velocity impact; an explicit stress–strain law in agreement with experiment is obtained, and an explanation of sliding friction is given. Some broad implications and practical applications of the particle-wave view are discussed in the final chapter.

REFERENCES

1. V. Volterra, *Ann. Ecole Norm. Super.* **24**, 401–517 (1907).
2. A. E. H. Love, *The Mathematical Theory of Elasticity*, Cambridge University Press, Cambridge, 1927.
3. G. I. Taylor, *Proc. Roy. Soc. (London)*, **A145**, 362–404 (1934).
4. E. Orowan, *Z. Physik.*, **89**, 605–613 (1934); **89**, 614–633 (1934); **89**, 634–659 (1934).
5. M. Polyani, *Z. Physik.*, **89**, 660–664 (1934).
6. J. M. Burgers, *Proc. Acad. Sci. Amsterdam*, **42**, 293–325 (1939); **42**, 378–399 (1939).
7. F. R. N. Nabarro, *Advan. Phys.*, **1**, 269–394 (1952).
8. J. D. Eshelby, *Solid State Phys.*, **3**, 79–84 (1956).
9. R. B. Pond and E. Harrison, *Rev. Sci. Instr.*, **28**, 574 (1957); AFOSR Report 1516, *Deslip in Aluminum Single Crystal Specimens*, 1962.
10. P. B. Hirsch, R. W. Horne, and M. J. Whelan, *Dislocations and Mechanical Properties of Crystals*, Wiley, New York, 1956, pp. 92–115.
11. L. de Broglie, *Phil. Mag.*, **47**, 446–458 (1924).
12. A. Einstein, *Ann. Physik.*, **17**, 132–149 (1905).
13. C. Davisson and L. H. Germer, *Phys. Rev.*, **30**, 705–740 (1927).
14. G. P. Thompson, *Proc. Roy. Soc. (London)*, **A117**, 600–609 (1928).
15. E. Rupp, *Ann. Physik.*, **85**, 981–1012 (1928); *Z. Physik.*, **52**, 8–28 (1929).
16. B. L. Worsnop, *Nature*, **123**, 164–165 (1929).
17. W. H. Zinn, *Phys. Rev.*, **70**, 102A (1946); **71**, 752–757 (1947).
18. I. Estermann and O. Stern, *Z. Physik.*, **61**, 95–126 (1930).
19. T. H. Johnson, *Phys. Rev.*, **35**, 1299–1300 (1930); *J. Franklin Inst.*, **210**, 135–152 (1930); *Phys. Rev.*, **37**, 87 (1931); **37**, 847–861 (1931).
20. A. Ellet, H. Olson, and H. Zahl, *Phys. Rev.*, **34**, 493–501 (1929).
21. S. Kikuchi, *Proc. Imp. Acad. Japan*, **4**, 271–274, 275–278, 354–356, 471–474 (1928); *Japan J. Phys.*, **51**, 83 (1928).
22. K. Knauer and O. Stern, *Z. Physik.*, **53**, 779–791 (1929).
23. H. E. Farnsworth, *Phys. Rev.*, **34**, 679–696 (1929); **35**, 1131–1133 (1930); **40**, 684–712 (1932); **43**, 900–910 (1933); **49**, 598–605, 605–609 (1936).
24. Described by Z. G. Pinsker, *Electron Diffraction*, Butterworths, London, 1953, Chapter 13, p. 386.
25. L. H. Germer, A. U. MacRae, and C. D. Hartman, *J. Appl. Phys.*, **32**, 2432–2439 (1961); L. H. Germer, E. J. Scheibner, and C. D. Hartman, *Phil. Mag.*, **5**, 222–236 (1960); L. H. Germer and C. D. Hartman, *J. Appl. Phys.*, **31**, 2085–2095 (1960).

26. A. Ellet and H. Olson, *Phys. Rev.*, **31**, 643–647 (1928).
27. J. B. Taylor, *Phys. Rev.*, **35**, 375–380 (1930).
28. H. A. Zahl, *Phys. Rev.*, **35**, 293 (1930); **36**, 893 (1930).
29. E. Schroedinger, *Ann. Physik.*, **79**, 361–376 (1926); **79**, 489–527 (1926); **80**, 437–490 (1926); **81**, 109–139 (1926).
30. M. Born, *Z. Physik.*, **37**, 863–867 (1926); **38**, 803 (1926).
31. L. Pauling and E. B. Wilson, *Introduction to Quantum Mechanics*, McGraw-Hill, New York, 1935, pp. 50–58.
32. D. Bohm, *Quantum Theory*, Prentice Hall, Englewood Cliffs, New Jersey, 1951.
33. A. Einstein, B. Podolsky, and N. Rosen, *Phys. Rev.*, **47**, 777 (1935); *Albert Einstein: Philosopher-Scientist*, P. S. Schlipp, Ed., Evanston Press, 1949.
34. M. Planck, *Physikalische Abhandlungen und Vorträge*, Band II, III, Vieweg, Braunschweig, 1958.
35. E. Schroedinger, *Naturwissenschaften*, **23**, 787–822, 823–843, 844–846 (1935).
36. W. Renninger, *Z. Physik.*, **136**, 251–261 (1935); **158**, 417–421 (1960).
37. L. de Broglie, *The Current Interpretation of Wave Mechanics, A Critical Study*, Elsevier, Amsterdam, 1964.
38. R. G. J. Fraser, *Molecular Rays*, Cambridge University Press, London, 1931, pp. 112–113.
39. M. Born and T. von Karman, *Physik. Z.*, **13**, 297–309 (1912); **14**, 15–19 (1913).
40. R. A. Smith, *Wave Mechanics of Crystalline Solids*, Wiley, New York, 1961.
41. P. C. Fine, *Phys. Rev.* **56**, 355–359 (1939).
42. R. B. Leighton, *Rev. Mod. Phys.*, **20**, 165–174 (1948).
43. See Appendix B, p. 202.

II

CHARACTERISTIC FREQUENCIES
OF DEFORMATION

Introduction

In the previous chapter, a new view of non-elastic deformation in solids was proposed in which particle momentum waves play a key role. A differential equation for such waves was set up and a solution found for infinitely large monatomic lattices, giving a frequency dependence on wave vector, k, in terms of Planck's constant, the crystal spacing, and atomic mass. Brief mention was made of the occurrence of discrete values of wave vector and frequency for finite lattices, and it is to these characteristic frequencies of deformation that we now turn in this second chapter. The presence of such discrete frequencies leads directly to the idea that a crystalline solid undergoing an oscillating load or vibration might respond with increased amplitude (resonate) when excited at a particular frequency corresponding to one of the characteristic particle wave modes. A calculation of the characteristic frequencies, in terms of crystal properties, is needed to allow specific predictions for comparison with experiment, and these calculations are carried out in the following treatment. The possibility of vibrations or acoustic emissions accompanying unidirectional deformation is also considered and compared with experimental observations.

1. Particle Waves in Finite Lattices

In considering the effect of a finite lattice or segment length on the propagation of a real property, ψ_n, of the type previously defined, it is important to note that the absence of a mass (atom) at a lattice point will necessarily result in fixing the amplitude of the propagated wave at zero for all times at that point. That is, we have specified that the property in question, ψ_n, can only be defined in the vicinity of the mass points of the lattice and not elsewhere. Of course, we can also imagine a situation in which a lattice mass is fixed or pinned so that its displacement is zero for all times. In either case, a finite lattice segment exists between two such points, as shown schematically in a two-dimensional lattice in Figure 2.1. If the end points at 0 and N are fixed so that their displacements are zero for all times, it follows that the velocities of these points are also zero for all time. That is,

$$x_0(t) = 0 \text{ and } x_N(t) = 0 \qquad \text{for all } t$$

then

$$v_0(t) = (\partial x / \partial t)_{x=x_0} = 0$$

$$v_N(t) = (\partial x / \partial t)_{x=x_N} = 0 \qquad (2.1)$$

In terms of the segment shown, there are fixed masses at 0 and N with $N-1$ masses between, and the segment length is $S = Nd$ where d is the lattice spacing. Momentum transfer through such a finite lattice segment must again occur according to the differential equation proposed in the first chapter, which is reproduced below in terms of the net momentum transfer at some general nth point of the segment:

$$m \frac{\partial v_n}{\partial t} = \mathbf{K}_p (v_{n+1} + v_{n-1} - 2v_n) \qquad (2.2)$$

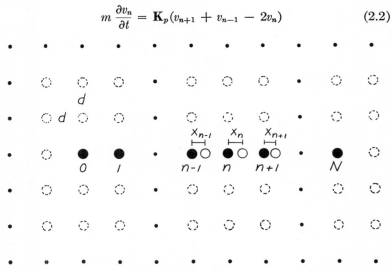

Fig. 2.1. A finite segment (filled circles) in a two-dimensional crystal lattice (dashed circles). End points 0 and N are fixed, and the unfilled solid circles represent displacements of the $n - 1$, n, and $n + 1$ masses (atoms) from their equilibrium positions.

Because of the condition of zero velocity at the segment ends, a standing wave solution is now suggested

$$v_n(t) = (B_1 e^{iknd} + B_2 e^{-iknd})\, e^{-i2\pi \nu_p t} \tag{2.3}$$

The condition that $v_0(0) = 0$ requires that $B_1 = -B_2$ so that

$$v_n(t) = B_1 e^{-i2\pi \nu_p t}\, 2i \sin kn\boldsymbol{d} \tag{2.4}$$

The condition that $v_N(0) = 0$ requires in addition that

$$\sin kN\boldsymbol{d} = 0$$

or

$$kN\boldsymbol{d} = q\pi$$

$$k = q\pi/N\boldsymbol{d} \tag{2.5}$$

where

$$q = 1, 2, 3 \ldots (N-1)$$

Hence, discrete values of k are now demanded. The necessary conditions on ν_p for Eqs. 2.3 and 2.4 to be solutions of the differential equation is again found to be that

$$\nu_p = \frac{2K_p}{\pi m} \sin^2 \frac{k\boldsymbol{d}}{2} \tag{2.6}$$

where $\mathbf{K}_p = iK_p$ as before. This is the same form of ν–k dependence found for an infinite lattice, but now discrete values of k are required, according to Eq. 2.5. A maximum value for ν_p occurs near $\lambda = 2\boldsymbol{d}$ when $q = N - 1$, for then

$$k = \frac{N-1}{N\boldsymbol{d}}\,\pi \cong \pi/\boldsymbol{d} \qquad (N \text{ large})$$

and

$$\nu_p(\max) = \frac{2K_p}{\pi m} = \frac{\hbar}{\pi m \boldsymbol{d}^2} \tag{2.7}$$

since $K_p = \hbar/2d^2$, as demonstrated in the first chapter. Now there is also a *lower* (nonzero) limit on ν_p near $\lambda = 2S$ given by setting $q = 1$, so that

$$k = \pi/Nd = \pi/S$$

leading to

$$\nu_p(\min) \cong \left(\frac{\pi}{2N}\right)^2 \nu_p(\max) \quad (N \text{ large})$$

$$\cong \frac{h}{8mS^2} \tag{2.8}$$

The same type of result is already well known for elastic displacement waves propagating through a finite one-dimensional lattice.[1] That is, given the differential equation for elastic displacement of a general nth point

$$m\,\frac{\partial^2 x_n}{\partial t^2} = K_e(x_{n+1} + x_{n-1} - 2x_n) \tag{2.9}$$

there is a solution

$$x_n(t) = A_1 e^{-i2\pi\nu_e t}\, 2i \sin knd \tag{2.10}$$

where

$$\nu_e = \frac{1}{\pi}\sqrt{\frac{K_e}{m}} \sin\frac{kd}{2} \tag{2.11}$$

and

$$k = q\pi/Nd$$

$$q = 1, 2, 3 \ldots (N - 1)$$

Maximum and minimum frequencies occur near $\lambda = 2d$ and $\lambda = 2S$, respectively,

$$\nu_e(\max) = \frac{1}{\pi}\sqrt{\frac{K_e}{m}} \tag{2.12}$$

$$\nu_e(\min) = \left(\frac{\pi}{2N}\right)\nu_e(\max) \tag{2.13}$$

The occurrence of discrete modes (k values) is not a unique property of standing waves and lattice segments with fixed ends. A long-range periodic variation (superstructure) or periodic boundary condition imposed on an infinite lattice will lead to discrete modes for running waves, as first demonstrated by Born and von Karmen[2] for elastic displacement waves. Suppose, for example, that at certain intervals, $S = Nd$, in an infinite lattice, the displacements are equal (but not zero), so that for all times

$$x_n(t) = x_{n+N}(t) \tag{2.14}$$

This means that the running-wave solution to the differential equation for elastic displacement in a lattice must be such that

$$Ae^{-i(2\pi\nu_e t - knd)} = Ae^{-i[2\pi\nu_e t - k(n+N)d]} \tag{2.15}$$

or

$$kNd = \pm 2\pi q$$

$$k = \pm q 2\pi / Nd \tag{2.16}$$

$$q = 1, 2, 3 \ldots (N-1)/2$$

The frequency condition remains unchanged as given by Eq. 2.11, except that the necessary discrete values of k are now given by Eq. 2.16.

In just the same way, periodic boundary conditions can be applied to a particle momentum wave so that, for an infinite lattice of equal masses, the *velocities* of the masses are the same (but not necessarily zero) at certain intervals, $S = Nd$, along the lattice

$$v_n(t) = v_{n+N}(t) \tag{2.17}$$

for all values of t. Then the corresponding running-wave solution to the differential equation for momentum transfer in the lattice must be such that

$$Be^{-i(2\pi\nu_p t - knd)} = Be^{-i[2\pi\nu_p t - k(n+N)d]} \tag{2.18}$$

or

$$kNd = \pm 2\pi q$$

$$k = \pm q 2\pi / Nd \tag{2.19}$$

$$q = 1, 2, 3 \ldots (N-1)/2$$

where again the frequency condition for ν_p is the same as for the standing-wave case (Eq. 2.6), but where the discrete values of q are taken according to Eq. 2.19 instead of Eq. 2.5.

The value of $q = 0$ is excluded, since this corresponds to $k = 0$ and infinite wavelength (all particles moving together). Similarly,

$q = N/2$ corresponds to $k = \pi/\boldsymbol{d}$ and zero group velocity, which must be excluded for running waves. The total number of modes $(N - 1)$ is the same as that for standing waves in lattices with fixed ends, since there are $(N - 1)/2$ running wave modes in each of two directions. The *density* of modes, dq/dk, in k space is different as seen below, where dq is the number of modes between k and $k + dk$ in each case;

$$dq/dk = N\boldsymbol{d}/2\pi \qquad \text{(running waves)}$$

$$dq/dk = N\boldsymbol{d}/\pi \qquad \text{(standing waves)}$$

The discrete frequencies for both elastic and particle waves are shown in Figure 2.2 as a function of wave vector, k, for $N = 21$. Since

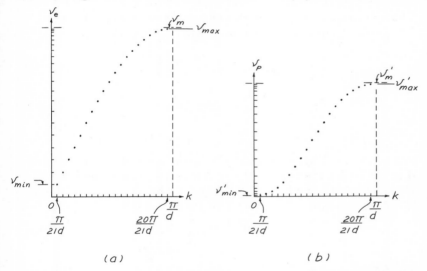

(a)   (b)

Fig. 2.2. (a) Frequency vs. wave vector, k, for an elastic displacement wave in a finite, one-dimensional lattice of spacing, $\boldsymbol{d}$, and length, $S = N\boldsymbol{d}$. In general, $N - 1$ discrete values of frequency are allowed at equal intervals along the k axis. The case shown is for $N = 21$, with 20 discrete values of k between $\pi/21\boldsymbol{d}$ and $20\pi/21\boldsymbol{d}$ at intervals of $\pi/21\boldsymbol{d}$. For larger values of N, the upper limit of k approaches $\pi/\boldsymbol{d}$. (b) Frequency vs. wave vector for a particle momentum wave in a finite, one-dimensional lattice, as in (a). The case shown is again for $N = 21$. Although the discrete values of k are evenly spaced for both elastic and particle waves, the frequency intervals are not constant nor the same for the two kinds of waves.

values of k are evenly spaced, the allowed particle-wave frequencies are closely spaced or bunched both at $k = 0$ and $k = \pi/d$, whereas the elastic frequencies are bunched only at the upper end ($k = \pi/d$).

2. The Frequency Spectrum

The preceding remarks on density of frequency modes can be made more precise by a determination of the frequency distribution of modes over the spectrum of allowed frequencies in a lattice. In order to accomplish this, we first define a particle-wave frequency distribution function $Z_p(\nu)$ such that $Z_p(\nu)d\nu_p$ equals the number of modes between ν_p and $\nu_p + d\nu_p$ in the interval in integer space between q and $q + dq$. That is

$$Z_p(\nu)d\nu_p = dq \qquad (2.20)$$

For convenience, the expression for particle-wave frequency given by Eq. 2.6 for a finite lattice can be written in terms of q as

$$\nu_{pq} = \nu_1 \sin^2\left(\frac{q\pi}{2N}\right) \qquad (2.21)$$

where

$$\nu_1 = h/2m\pi^2 d^2 \qquad (2.22)$$

for

$$q = 1, 2, 3 \ldots (N - 1)$$

and where h is Planck's constant, m is the mass of the lattice atoms, d is the lattice spacing, and $S = Nd$ is the lattice segment length. Upon differentiating Eq. 2.21 with respect to q and substituting into Eq. 2.20, we obtain

$$Z_p(\nu) = \frac{N}{\pi\nu_1 \sin\frac{q\pi}{2N} \cos\frac{q\pi}{2N}} \qquad (2.23)$$

The distribution function thus has singularities [i.e., $Z_p(\nu) \to \infty$] at $q = 0$ and $q = N$, and a minimum of $2N/\pi\nu_1$ at $q = N/2$. Since ν_p and q are related by Eq. 2.21, we can also write this distribution function in terms of ν_p

$$Z_p(\nu) = \frac{N}{\pi\nu_p^{1/2}\nu_1^{1/2} \cos(\arcsin\sqrt{\nu_p/\nu_1})} \qquad (2.24)$$

This function is infinite when $\nu_p = 0$ and $\nu_p = \nu_1$, and has a minimum of $2N/\pi\nu_1$ when $\nu_p = \nu_1/2$, as shown in Figure 2.3. The dashed line

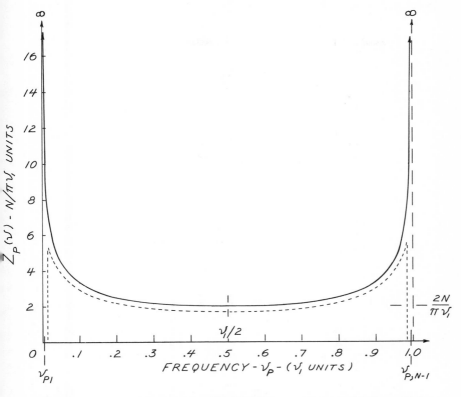

Fig. 2.3. Frequency distribution function (frequency spectrum) for particle waves in a crystal. The envelope function extends from zero to ν_1, but is cut off or bounded at ν_{p1} and $\nu_{p,N-1}$ for a lattice segment of length, $N\boldsymbol{d}$. The dashed curve shows the bounded function for a smaller value of N (exaggerated).

shows the frequency distribution function for a smaller value of N (and thus S).

The corresponding distribution function for elastic waves in a one-dimensional finite lattice is

$$Z_e(\nu) = \frac{2N}{\pi \nu_m \cos\left[\arcsin\left(\nu_e/\nu_m\right)\right]} \qquad (2.25)$$

where

$$\nu_m = \frac{1}{\pi} \sqrt{\frac{K_e}{m}}$$

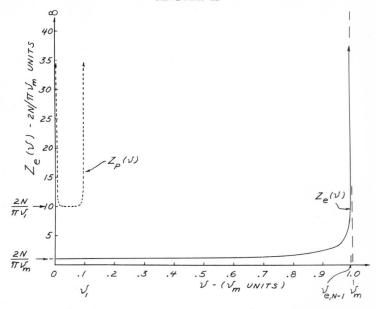

Fig. 2.4. Frequency spectrum for elastic waves in a one-dimensional crystal. Dashed curve gives the particle-wave frequency spectrum of Figure 3 for comparison. In addition to having no singularity at $\nu = 0$, the elastic wave spectrum has an upper cutoff frequency, ν_m, about 400 times that for a particle wave, ν_1, in the same crystal, but curves are shown for $\nu_m = 10\nu_1$.

We note that the elastic distribution function has no singularity at $\nu_e = 0$, but starts at a value of $2N/\pi\nu_m$ and rises to infinity only at $\nu_e = \nu_m$, as shown in Figure 2.4. A comparison of the frequency spectra for elastic and particle waves is given in Figure 2.4, where ν_m is arbitrarily taken as 10 ν_1. Actually, as we shall see, in real materials ν_m is usually about 400 ν_1. The frequency spectrum for particle waves is of the same form for any direction in a three-dimensional lattice, according to the results obtained in the first chapter; only the value of ν_1 (which depends on the lattice spacing, d), changes with direction in the lattice. In close-packed directions, the particle-wave spectrum for a given N will be broader and lower than in other directions.

By contrast to the case for particle waves, frequency spectra for elastic waves in three-dimensional monatomic lattices consist of three branches which may be added to get the total distribution function, as indicated in Figure 2.5 for a body-centered cubic crystal

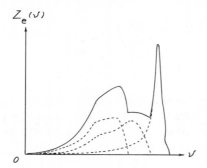

Fig. 2.5. Frequency spectrum for elastic waves in three-dimensional (bcc) crystals. Solid line represents total spectrum and dashed lines represent component spectra. From data of Fine.[3]

(Fine,[3] 1939). Similar elastic frequency spectra have been calculated for other types of lattices, including simple cubic,[4] face-centered cubic,[5] alkali halides,[6] and diamond.[7] In all cases, maxima or peaks occur only at the high-frequency ends of these spectra, and values of $Z_e(\nu)$ at low frequencies are always very small.

The sharp rise in the particle-wave distribution function, $Z_p(\nu)$, at low frequencies is therefore unusual and of great interest.

The particle-wave frequency spectrum arising from periodic boundary conditions leads to the same result as that for a finite lattice segment, as shown elsewhere.[8]

3. Audio-Frequency Modes

The sharp rise in the particle-wave frequency spectrum, and consequent accumulation of modes at low frequencies, suggests that vibration of a crystal at low frequencies in some range might result in an abnormal response, in the same way that solids resonate at elastic modes. Now, however, the resonant frequencies or modes will depend on the internal lattice segment lengths, S, rather than external sample dimensions. The explicit expressions for the discrete particle-wave frequencies are, for standing and running waves, respectively,

$$\nu_{pq} = \nu_1 \sin^2 \left(\frac{q\pi}{2N} \right) \qquad \text{(standing waves)} \qquad (2.26)$$

$$q = 1, 2, 3 \ldots (N - 1)$$

$$\nu_{pq} = \nu_1 \sin^2 \left(\frac{q\pi}{N} \right) \qquad \text{(running waves)} \qquad (2.27)$$

$$q = 1, 2, 3 \ldots (N-1)/2$$

The frequency spectrum is the same for both types of waves, and for large values of N both types will have an upper frequency limit of ν_1. The low-frequency minima are quite different for the two cases, however, as indicated below

$$\nu_{p1} = \frac{h}{8mN^2 d^2} \qquad \text{(standing wave)} \qquad (2.28)$$

$$\nu_{p1} = \frac{h}{2mN^2 d^2} \qquad \text{(running wave)} \qquad (2.29)$$

For convenience in discussing low-frequency modes, we recall that the sine of angle can be approximated by the angle at low values. As a practical matter, this turns out to mean that $\sin \theta$ can be replaced by θ (in radians) for $\theta \leq \pi/18$ (10°) without introducing any error greater than 0.4%; correspondingly, values of $\sin^2 \theta$ can be replaced by θ^2 to within less than 1% error. For low frequencies, Eqs. 2.26 and 2.27 then become

$$\nu_{pq} = \frac{h}{8mS^2} q^2 \qquad \text{(standing waves)} \qquad (2.26')$$

and

$$\nu_{pq} = \frac{h}{2mS^2} q^2 \qquad \text{(running waves)} \qquad (2.27')$$

where

$$q = 1, 2, 3 \ldots (N/9)$$

and $S = Nd$ is the segment length or long-range periodicity.

The magnitudes of these low-frequency modes will depend on the value of S; it is not easy to decide on a *precise* value for this quantity in a real crystal, but there is a preponderance of evidence that S is about 10^{-4} cm in many cases. Values of S in this range lead to low-frequency modes in the audio range, as will be demonstrated after a brief citation of some of the evidence for the existence of substructure (segments) in crystals.

Early x-ray work by Darwin[9] and Ewald[10] indicated that real crystals consist of slightly misoriented blocks or domains, and recent work has confirmed the existence of substructures within single crystals or grains of polycrystals. Furthermore, the occurrence and size of the substructures is known to depend on the prior deformation, cold-working, and annealing treatment of the materials. Thus, Dunn and Daniels[11] have reported domain widths from 5.1 to 2.2×10^{-4} cm in silicon–iron single crystals which were deformed to various extents and annealed for 10 minutes at 950°C. The smallest width was found for the most severely deformed crystal. After 24 hours at 950°C, the domain widths ranged from 18.3 to 3.7×10^{-4} cm in these same crystals. Higher annealing temperatures produced further increases in width up to 42.5×10^{-4} cm.

Heidenreich[12] has used electron-microscope transmission to show that pure polycrystalline aluminum, heavily worked at room temperature, consists of slightly misoriented domains about 2×10^{-4} cm across. The domain size remained the same even after the sample was allowed to rest at room temperature for a year and the internal strain within the domains had entirely disappeared. Beck and Hu[13] confirmed these results on heavily rolled aluminum, and Kellar, Hirsch, and Thorp[14] used an x-ray microbeam method to show that pure aluminum worked at room temperature had domains about 3.6×10^{-4} wide, which decreased to 2.2×10^{-4} cm after prolonged resting at room temperature. Barrett[15] has shown that the etched surface of a high-purity copper grain reveals the presence of elongated blocks or rods from 0.1×10^{-4} to 0.5×10^{-4} cm wide and from 1×10^{-4} to 5×10^{-4} cm long within the grain. Numerous other investigations support the general view that most real single crystals or polycrystals contain many slightly misoriented (1–2 minutes) blocks or domains ranging in size from 10^{-3} to 10^{-5} cm across. In an excellent summary of the mosaic structure of crystals, Hirsch,[16] for example, lists 369 references in which evidence of this type is given.

A sample calculation for aluminum, based on $S = 10^{-4}$ cm, gives the first few standing-wave modes, as indicated below

$$\nu_{p1} = 1850 \text{ cps}$$

$$\nu_{p2} = 7400 \text{ cps}$$

$$\nu_{p3} = 16,650 \text{ cps}$$

etc.

A segment length of 10^{-4} cm corresponds to $N \cong 3500$ for aluminum, where $d_1 = 2.86 \times 10^{-8}$ cm is the distance of closest approach (slip direction). The highest particle-wave frequency can be calculated directly from the crystal spacing, atomic mass, and Planck's constant, according to Eq. 2.22. For aluminum, it is

$$\nu_{p,N-1} \cong \nu_1 = 8.25 \times 10^9 \text{ cps}$$

By way of comparison, the corresponding minimum and maximum *elastic* (shear) wave frequencies for a lattice segment length of 10^{-4} cm in aluminum are 1.64×10^9 and 3.65×10^{12} cps, respectively. To put it another way, the elastic wavelength corresponding to a frequency of 1850 cps in aluminum is about 175 cm instead of 2×10^{-4} cm, as it is for particle waves.

It is also easily demonstrated that changes in segment length, S, will produce large *relative* changes in the particle-wave modes at low frequencies. That is if $\Delta\nu_p$ is the change in frequency produced by a change $\Delta S = \Delta N d$ in segment length, then $\Delta\nu_p$ (low) $= \Delta\nu_p$ (high), but

$$\frac{\Delta\nu_p}{\nu_{p1}} \gg \frac{\Delta\nu_p}{\nu_{p,N-1}} \tag{2.28}$$

In the aluminum example, if N is increased from 3500 to $N' = 7000$, the absolute value of $\Delta\nu_p$ for both high and low frequencies is 1388 cps, but the *relative* changes are

$$\frac{\Delta\nu_p}{\nu_{p1}} \text{ (low)} = -1388/1850 = -75\%$$

$$\frac{\Delta\nu_p}{\nu_{p,N-1}} \text{ (high)} = 1388/8.25 \times 10^9 = 1.7 \times 10^{-5}\%$$

From these typical results, it is clear that the audio-frequency end of the particle-wave spectrum will be extremely sensitive to any changes in a real crystal which vary the lattice segment lengths.

Another question must be: Are standing waves or running waves present in a given case? This is equivalent to asking how the mosaic structure effects the lattice; will the momentum be zero at domain boundaries or merely have the same nonzero values? Vacancies and other lattice irregularities can be expected to occur near the domain boundaries, and the possibility is therefore strong that an actual pinning or fixing of lattice segments occurs at domain boundaries. On the other hand, it is equally conceivable that periodic changes in momentum occur at intervals equal to the domain widths. In particular, the momentum waves might change *direction* at a boundary in order to follow the closest spacing and, hence, proceed through a crystal in a slight zigzag fashion. Perhaps both types of waves are always present.

4. Resonance Dispersion and Some Experimental Results

The existence of an accumulation of particle-wave modes at low frequencies, coupled with evidence for segment lengths around 10^{-4} cm, leads to the definite prediction that a crystal vibrated in the audio range should show a sharply rising response at one or more discrete frequencies, somewhere in the range between 10 and 20,000 cps. The resonances should be quite sharp if a well-defined mean segment length, S_0, exists in the crystal, but some broadening may result from a distribution of segment lengths.

As a matter of fact, the existence of such audio-frequency mechanical resonance modes in crystalline solids has been known for some time.[17]

Experimental results are given for two fcc polycrystalline metals (Al, Pb) in Figures 2.6 and 2.7. The results were obtained with an electromagnetic transducer apparatus which has been described in detail elsewhere,[17] but it is worth noting here that in this apparatus a complex mechanical admittance, $\mathbf{Y}_M$ = velocity/force, is measured for a pair of disk-shaped samples vibrated in shear. The real and imaginary parts of a complex shear compliance, $\mathbf{J}^*$, are then calculated from a knowledge of the cross-sectional area, A, and the thickness, b, of each sample disk, according to

$$\mathbf{J}^* = J' - iJ'' = i\,\frac{A}{b}\,\frac{\mathbf{Y}_M}{2\pi\nu} \tag{2.29}$$

Metal samples are machined to size and their surfaces lapped before testing; in addition, it is necessary to apply a static, clamping load to hold the samples between the shearing members of the apparatus so that samples tested are always under load.

From Figures 2.6 and 2.7, it can be seen that a large, sharp resonance occurs near 2900 cps in each of the metals shown. If this resonance is the first particle-wave mode of the most common segment length, S_0, in each case, then it might be supposed that this length must have been shorter in the lead than in the aluminum samples. This follows, since the product mS_0^2 could then be constant (the atomic mass of lead is about 7.5 times that of aluminum). Thus, for a segment length in aluminum approximately 2.7 times that in lead, a constant frequency, ν_{p1}, could exist.

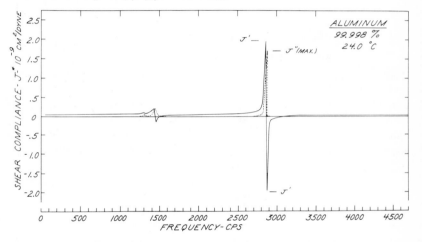

Fig. 2.6. Variation of complex shear compliance, $\mathbf{J^*} = J' - iJ''$, with frequency of shearing force for polycrystalline aluminum (99.998%) at room temperature. From data of Fitzgerald.[17]

The resonances are quite sharp (100–200-cps wide), which could result from a narrow grouping of segment lengths around a common value, S_0. Aluminum shows a second peak near 1400 cps of about one-sixth the strength of the peak at 2900 cps. The lead sample also originally showed additional peaks near 1000, 1600, 1880, and 2640 cps. The peak near 1000 cps shifted rapidly to higher frequencies with time, and all of the lead peaks except the one near 2900 cps disappeared when the sample was heated for 15 hours at 150°C.

The resonances are not confined to fcc polycrystalline metals, but have been observed in single crystals,[18] crystalline polymers,[17] and organic crystals.[19] Results for a sodium chloride single crystal[18] are adduced in Figure 2.8 and indicate clearly that resonances are not confined to monatomic crystals or to metals. A mode near 2900 cps is again the main one, but additional modes appear. In the sodium chloride samples tested, there were 14 resonance peaks between 100 and 5000 cps. Sharp resonances of this same type have been reported

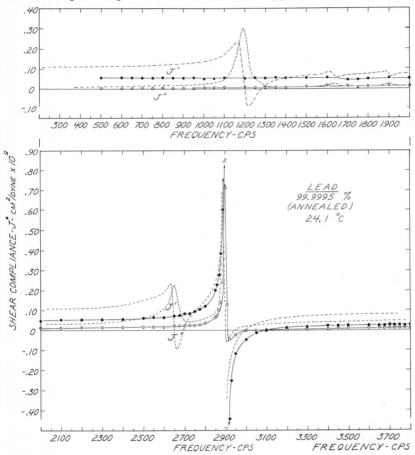

Fig. 2.7. Variation of complex shear compliance, $\mathbf{J}^* = J' - iJ''$, with frequency of shearing force for polycrystalline lead (99.999%) after annealing at 150°C for 15 hours. Results on machined samples before annealing are shown by dashed lines. From data of Fitzgerald.[17]

in complex shear-compliance measurements on indium,[17] tool steel,[20] germanium single crystals,[20] quartz crystals,[21] crystalline polymers like polyethylene,[22] polytetrafluoroethylene,[17] poly(vinyl stearate),[23] and organic crystals, such as vinyl and ethyl stearate and normal paraffins.[24]

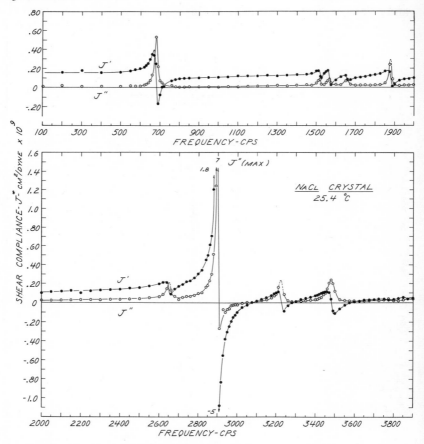

Fig. 2.8. Variation of complex shear compliance, $J^* = J' - iJ''$, with frequency of shearing force (in < 100 > direction) for sodium chloride single crystals. From data of Fitzgerald.[18]

In all cases, the effects of factors such as static loading, stress history, x-irradiation, hardening, and annealing[20] suggested strongly that the resonances were closely connected with the defect-modified (e.g., the mosaic pattern) structures of the materials. In terms of our discussion, it is clear that the effective segment length or lengths must be a critical factor. The orientation of segments, as well as their lengths, may also be an important consideration in producing a combined sample response to macroscopic vibrations.

The effect of orientation, as well as segment length, can be uniquely seen in lightly vulcanized natural rubber (hevea), where reversible changes from a completely amorphous state to an ordered crystalline state can be produced at constant temperature by purely mechanical means, i.e., by stretching. The stretch-induced crystallinity in vulcanized natural rubber has been extensively studied by a number of investigators using both x-ray and thermodynamic techniques. The results for many lightly vulcanized gum stocks (1–3 wt.-% of sulfur) show that, at temperatures around 25°C, crystallization of the originally amorphous rubber appears first at an elongation of about 300%, i.e., when the stretched length is four times the original length. Thus, Hauser and Mark[25] have reported data in which x-ray spots appeared in place of amorphous rings at 300% elongation; Goppel[26] obtained results in which the first detectable crystallinity (4%) occurred at 300% elongation in a natural rubber stock with 1.75 parts sulfur per 100 parts rubber; Gehman and Field[27] found the minimum elongation for diffraction spots in the x-ray patterns to be 300% for a rubber stock with 1.5 parts sulfur; and Wildschut[28] deduced, from tension–temperature relations, crystallinities of less than 1% below 300% elongation; these rose sharply at 275–300%, however, and reached values of 25% crystallinity at 500% elongation. Recently, Yau and Stein (1963,1964)[29] have investigated stretched rubber at room temperature by means of low-angle light scattering using a laser photographic technique. They report evidence for a crystalline *superstructure* which first appears around 200% elongation, but is pronounced above 300%. The angle at which the scattering occurs is about 10° and, thus, corresponds to a structure size of the order of 2×10^{-4} cm. As a result of the scattering patterns, Yau and Stein reached a number of conclusions in addition to the principal one that superstructures of the order of 2×10^{-4} cm are formed in stretched rubber. These are:

(1) The optical heterogeneities, giving evidence of the superstructure, are not present in unstretched samples since scattering patterns are not present.

(2) The patterns disappear when the samples are released after stretching.

(3) The scattering does not arise from a variation in density, average polarization, or degree of crystallinity from place to place, but from a variation in orientation of some anisotropic body of about 2×10^{-4} cm length.

(4) Patterns with a single streak, such as that found at 300%, indicate that the large scattering structure is aligned parallel to the stretching direction, but the split patterns at higher elongations indicate a structure with its maximum dimension at about 20° to the stretching direction.

These remarks on stretched rubber have a direct bearing on our ideas about the existence of particle-wave modes at audio frequencies in crystals, for such modes, in accordance with our line of thought, should be present in stretched (crystalline) rubber, but not in unstretched (amorphous) rubber. Further, the discovery of a crystalline superstructure of definite length allows a calculation of the exact frequency to be expected. Rubber is not monatomic, but contains both carbon and hydrogen. However, the principal bonds are those between carbon atoms, so that we may safely calculate the lowest standing-wave mode according to Eq. 2.26' by using the mass of a carbon atom. This lowest mode is

$$\nu_{p1} = \frac{6.62 \times 10^{-27}}{8 \cdot 1.99 \times 10^{-23} (2 \times 10^{-4})^2}$$

$$= 1040 \text{ cps}$$

for stretched natural rubber, and should appear at an elongation just above 300%. This value may be compared with the actual experimental results found in dynamic shear-compliance measurements on stretched rubber three years earlier,[30] as shown in Figure 2.9. The measurements were made in the direction of stretching, and the observed large resonance which first appeared at 310% elongation was

$$\nu_{\text{exp}} = 1020 \text{ cps}$$

After 74 hours at 310% elongation, this resonance had shifted to 1105 cps and at 350 and 400% elongations it appeared at 1200 cps. Even

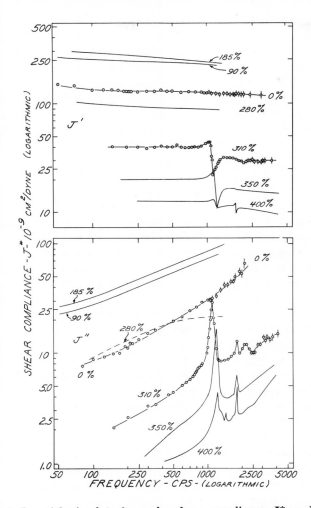

Fig. 2.9. Logarithmic plot of complex shear compliance, $\mathbf{J^*} = J' - iJ''$, vs. frequency for natural rubber at various static elongations, as indicated. Results above 300% varied with time; the curves shown are for approximately equilibrium conditions (i.e., after 80 hours). Temperature was 25.1 ± 0.2°C. Experimental points are shown for 0 and 310% elongations, but are otherwise omitted to avoid confusion. Note that the sharp peak near 1000 cps appeared first at an elongation of 310%, and thus coincides with the occurrence of both a crystallinity and a superstructure, as discussed in the text. From data of Fitzgerald.[30]

these shifts can be accounted for, however, in terms of the tilting of the superstructure observed in the light-scattering measurements. A shift from 1020 to 1200 cps is equivalent to a decrease in effective segment length to 0.92 times the original value (i.e., from 2 to 1.85 $\times$ 10^{-4} cm). Such a decrease can be accounted for in terms of the observed tilt of the superstructure of around 20° at elongations above 300%, since the effective segment length, S_0', in the direction of stretching (and shear vibration) would then be

$$S_0' = S_0 \cos 20°$$

$$S_0'/S_0 = \cos 20° = 0.94$$

The existence of particle-wave modes in crystalline materials at audio frequencies resulting from lattice segments about 10^{-4} cm long is strongly confirmed by these results, which represent the first successful calculation of a mechanical quantity involving Planck's constant.

All of the previous measurements were made on samples of very small size (largest dimension, 2 cm or less), so that the presence of normal elastic modes was precluded below about 75,000 cps. Evidence for these same resonances has been reported also in free-free bar measurements with the bar under tensile load applied by long, thin wires.[31,32] In these cases, the size of the specimen was increased so that elastic and particle-wave modes were present simultaneously at audio frequencies. This is possible because the particle-wave modes are determined by the internal segment length, S_0, of the crystalline superstructure or mosaic blocks comprising the sample, and do not necessarily vary with the sample size. Thus, in the transverse vibration experiments with bars, the tension on the bar may be adjusted to produce internal segment lengths or orientations that give particle-wave frequencies near one of the elastic-mode frequencies of the bar. The result is that multiple sharp peaks appear in the response vs. frequency curve for the bar in the region of some of the elastic modes, as shown in Figure 2.10 for a crystalline polymer bar four inches long and of one-fourth inch diameter. Without tension, the particle-wave modes are not present, so that we may conclude that some superstructures of the order of 10^{-4} cm are induced or perhaps lined up by the tension, as is the case for stretched natural rubber. Hence, the elastic response will scale up or down with, and depend on, the sample size, but the overall particle-wave contribution to the macro-

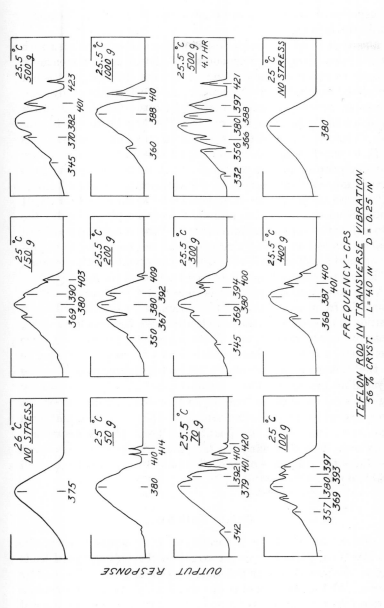

Fig. 2.10. Traces of output responses vs. driving frequency for a polytetrafluoroethylene rod (4.0-in. long and 1/4 in. in diameter) in free-free vibration under various axial loads applied by long thin wires, as discussed in the text. The rod was annealed for 4 hours at 200°C before the tests. From data of Fitzgerald and Woodward.[31]

scopic response of the sample will depend solely on internal segment sizes and orientations.

The idea that there can be audio-frequency modes associated with the internal structure, but independent of the external dimensions, of a sample has been a difficult concept for some to accept. It is not to be expected that old habits of thought can be discarded easily, but, for interested persons, a simple method for observing particle-wave modes at audio frequencies has recently been outlined.[33,34] In this method, a piezoelectric agitator, A, is placed on a large stainless steel block, B, to which is attached a post and arm to hold an ordinary high-fidelity ceramic pickup cartridge, C. A is driven by any low-distortion audio oscillator capable of 1–2 watts output, and the voltage from C is read on a vacuum-tube voltmeter reading to about 0.01 millivolts. Several soft rubber grommets may be placed under the block to isolate the apparatus from random vibrations. Samples of test material are placed on A, and a rubber band can be arranged to provide a constant small pressure of C against the sample. If the response from C is now noted as a function of frequency with the agitator driving voltage constant, several narrow maxima in the output will be noted and the frequencies at which these occur will vary, depending on the position of the needle on the sample and other factors such as load, pretreatment of the sample, etc. These results have been cited since they represent a relatively inexpensive means for anyone wishing to verify the existence of non-elastic audio-frequency resonances in polycrystalline materials. The resonances can also be detected by placing one's ear close to the sample, so that even a voltmeter is not necessary except for quantitative results. In this way, we might even say that, in a certain sense, it is possible to "hear" Planck's constant.

In any case, it is a remarkable fact that this simple experiment demonstrates the existence of particle momentum waves beyond all reasonable doubt.

5. Acoustic Emission

The description of plastic deformation as a momentum-transfer process involving particle-wave propagation through a crystal leads directly to the idea that such deformation should be accompanied by vibrations. This follows because the progress of a particle wave through the lattice subjects each mass (atom) to an instantaneous force equal to the time rate of change of momentum. From the expression for the velocity of a general nth mass (Eq. 2.4), we can calculate $\partial v_n / \partial t$ and, hence, the force on such a general point

$$f_{pn}(t) = m\,\frac{\partial v_n}{\partial t} = (4\pi m B_1 \nu_p \sin kn\mathbf{d})\,e^{-i2\pi\nu_p t} \qquad (2.30)$$

where ν_p is given by Eq. 2.6. Thus, each mass in a lattice segment of length $S = N\mathbf{d}$ will experience an oscillating force of frequency, ν_p; only certain discrete values of ν_p will occur, but many of these will lie in the audio range for $S = 10^{-4}$ cm. The expression for the force at low frequencies can be written, in terms of the q integer and the approximation that $\sin^2 \theta = \theta^2$, as

$$f_{pn}(t) = \left(\frac{B_1 h}{S^2}\,\pi^2 q^2 \sin \frac{q\pi n}{N}\right) e^{-i2\pi\nu_{pq} t} \qquad q < N/9 \qquad (2.31)$$

For any mode, the amplitude of the oscillating force will vary along the segment length and is easily calculated as a function of n/N, as shown in Figure 2.11.

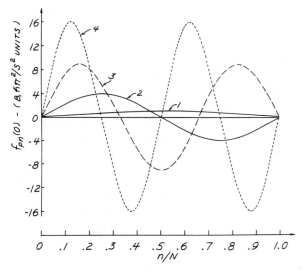

Fig. 2.11. Variation of amplitude with distance along a lattice segment, $n\mathbf{d}$, for the force on each mass (atom) produced by particle-wave momentum transfer along the lattice. Only the first four modes of the particle-wave spectrum ($q = 1, 2, 3, 4$) are shown.

From this figure, it is clear that there will be no net translational force on the segment as a whole for even modes, but, for odd modes, there will be a *net* oscillating translational force over the entire segment. Such a net force will tend to set into vibration the crystal sample as a whole, in the same way that an external oscillating force (applied over some portion of the sample surface) produces vibration. By integrating the force, f_{pn}, over the entire segment length, the net amplitude, A_q, can be found for any mode

$$A_q = \frac{B_1 h}{S^2} N q \qquad (2.32)$$

$$q = 1, 3, 5, 7 \ldots$$

$$A_q = 0$$

$$q = 2, 4, 6, 8 \ldots$$

The expression for the net oscillating force over an entire segment thus becomes

$$f_q(t) = \frac{B_1 h}{N d^2} q e^{-i2\pi \nu_{pq} t} \qquad (2.33)$$

$$q = 1, 3, 5 \ldots < N/9$$

An estimate of the mean force amplitude per unit length along a segment 10^{-4} cm long for $q = 1$ is about 2×10^{-8} dyne/cm.

We expect, therefore, that, as a usual matter, very small amplitude audio-frequency sounds will accompany the plastic deformation of crystals, unless somehow these add up or occur simultaneously throughout an appreciable volume of the sample so that stronger vibrations occur.

In discussing net translational forces on a lattice segment, contributions from even modes were absent. This is not to say that even modes do not contribute to crystal vibrations. On the contrary, it can be shown that even modes produce net oscillating torques or twisting forces in the crystal of the form (cf. Appendix D)

$$T_q(t) = \frac{B_1 h}{4 d} q (\cos q\pi + 1) e^{-i2\pi \nu_{pq} t} \qquad (2.34)$$

$$q = 2, 4, 6, 8 \ldots < N/9$$

The amplitudes of these torques are again small for each segment.

It can also be demonstrated that net oscillating translational forces and net oscillating torques result from running-wave modes in the lattice, as discussed in Appendix D.

We next ask what experimental evidence exists for audio-frequency or acoustic emission occuring during plastic deformation of crystals? As early as 1923, Portevin and Le Chatelier[35] reported a small sharp noise (petit bruit sec) accompanying stress jumps in aluminum alloys undergoing large deformation. The stress jumps were accompanied by the appearance of striations (Luder lines) on the surface of the sample, and each time the lines appeared a noise was heard, sometimes at a distance of several meters from the sample. In experiments beginning in 1924, Joffé[36] observed that a single crystal of rock salt plastically deformed at 450°C emitted cracking noises which were periodic and suggested the ticking of a clock. Similar noises were heard in zinc single crystals deformed at room temperature. Nekludova (1929)[37] subsequently carefully investigated the plastic deformation of rock salt, polycrystalline aluminum, and single and polycrystalline brass. In all cases, a jumplike deformation was observed; above 230°C, the rock-salt crystal deformation was again accompanied by periodic cracking noises like "the ticking of a clock." Aluminum deformation revealed sliding lines like those reported by Portevin and Le Chatelier, and crackling noises were also heard. The occurrence of similar crackling noises during deformation has probably been known to metal smiths working with tin, for example, long before any of these investigations. This "cry of tin" is also heard when zinc, cadmium, and indium are severely deformed. It has been related to the twinning process.[38] Other investigators have also reported sounds from metals during severe deformation.[39,40]

The occurrence of much fainter sounds at low stress levels and continuing through yield was reported in 1953 by Kaiser,[41] who used sensitive detectors with high amplification. The loading system must be very quiet in this type of measurement so that it does not generate external noise. Kaiser found audio-frequency sounds emanating from polycrystalline zinc, steel, aluminum, copper, lead, and wood when these materials were deformed.

An extensive investigation of the phenomena of acoustic emission, over a range of stress levels and on a number of polycrystalline and single-crystal metal samples, has been carried out since 1954 by Schofield.[42] Materials studied have included single crystals and polycrystals of zinc and aluminum, single crystals of gold, polycrystalline copper, lead, 24ST aluminum, cast tin, and carbon steel. The specimens were pulled in tension by use of a buoyancy-tank loading system, which is very quiet. Piezoelectric transducer stacks were coupled to the ends of the specimens by means of a thin oil film, and the signals from each during a test were amplified and recorded on tape, so that they could be analyzed and studied at any later time. The elongation of the sample was measured simultaneously, so that the time occurrence of any sound could be correlated with the deformation at that time. Various orientations of the single crystals were tested, as well as polycrystalline samples of several grain sizes.

One of the main conclusions reached by Schofield is that acoustic emission consists of two distinct types: (1) random, low-frequency, high-amplitude pulses or bursts; and (2) a continuous high-frequency emission initially of low amplitude, which increases in amplitude as the sample is stressed and deformed. According to Schofield, single crystals of zinc and aluminum exhibit the two extremes of isolated bursts vs. frequent or continuous emission, respectively. Analysis of the taped signals reveals that the frequency of the emission increases with load, along with increases in amplitude.

For steel specimens, there were chiefly signals between 2000 and 4000 cps at low stresses, but, as the stress was increased to its yield point, the predominant signals were from 4000 to 10,000 cps; no emission was observed in any steel specimens much above 16,000 to 20,000 cps. In 24ST-4 aluminum, the 3000-cps content was high at low stress, but decreased, and a strong 6000-cps contribution appeared at higher stress levels; the highest frequencies observed were 32,000 cps. At engineering yield (0.2% offset), sustained bursts are sometimes observed, and analysis of these showed frequencies of the order of 10^4 cps, for example, for an individual pulse in zinc. Tatro[43] has reported acoustic emission from work-hardened steel, in which bursts of longer duration (~ 0.5 sec) were observed near yield with frequencies of about 3×10^3 cps. Cusick[44] has observed acoustic emission in the range 300–10,000 cps in sodium chloride single crystals in four-point bending tests. He reported the chief frequencies of emission to be near 3000, 6000, and 9000 cps, with the amplitude of the 3000-cps emission considerably larger than that of the other frequencies. A load-deflection curve for the sodium chloride sample was measured simultaneously, and the emission is judged by him to be associated with a slip process. Liptai and Tatro[45] have also reported acoustic emission from aluminum single crystals in the range 2–20,000 cps, and associate it with the slip process.

The most complete description of the phenomenon is given by Schofield's work and we quote the following verbatum excerpt from one of his reports:[42]

A steady, low rate of stress loading is applied to a zinc single crystal. Almost immediately, as the load is applied, the burst-type signals appear. The signals occur suddenly in a random fashion at a relatively slow rate with the amplitudes of the individual pulses of assorted values. The rate of occurrence of the pulses increases slowly for a time, then increases markedly, producing a profusion of rapidly occurring pulses, the amplitude of some increasing considerably over the level of the early signals. Observance of these signals, amplified and passed through a loudspeaker gives the impression of many particles of metal colliding; tinkling and clanging sounds being evident. All of this occurs at very low strain levels and, as x-ray and microscopic examinations of the specimens have shown, without the appearance of twinning. As the specimen begins to deform grossly, the high frequency contribution becomes the major proportion of the total emission. This emission increases again very sharply just prior to failure.

Possible surface effects and the influence of oxide layers were investigated by Schofield in etching experiments on aluminum single crystals and in tests on gold single crystals. A summary of Schofield's principal conclusions from these and related tests follows:

(1) Two types of audio-frequency emission are observed in all metals—low-frequency pulses or bursts which may have large amplitudes at low stresses, and high-frequency continuous emission whose amplitude is small at low stresses, but increases with load.

(2) The amplitude of the emission is proportional to deformation rate.

(3) The emission is intimately related to permanent (i.e., non-elastic) deformation processes.

(4) There is evidence for a one-to-one correspondence between the number of fine-slip lines developed and the total number of pulses, at least at low stress levels where the pulses could be separated.

(5) Since emission is observed in the nominal "elastic" range of the materials well below yield, plastic deformation processes must be present at all stress levels, not just near or at yield.

(6) The acoustic emission is a volume effect originating inside the specimen and not purely a surface effect.

(7) The acoustic pulses are of extremely low energy, and amplifications of 10^6 to 10^7 are required for the detection of individual pulses. In some deformation processes (e.g., grain rotation, twinning), avalanches of pulses may occur to produce a combined signal of much more energy.

Finally, in view of the results cited from vibration experiments on stretched rubber, it is of interest to note that Powers (1963)[46] has reported the occurrence of "snapping noises" when certain crystalline polymers (including polytetrafluoroethylene) are compressed between diamond anvils.

Thus, it is apparent that our expectation of the occurrence of audio-frequency sounds or vibration, during deformation produced by uni-directional loads, is fulfilled. This expectation was based on the idea that the deformation process in question is one in which momentum is transferred through a crystal lattice via the propagation of particle waves. Individual vibrations or pulses are also of very small amplitude, as foreseen; only when large numbers occur together can they be heard directly without amplification. In many instances, certain frequencies, or a narrow range of frequencies, predominate.

The fact that the amplitude of the acoustic emission depends on deformation *rate* also indicates clearly that it is a *momentum-dependent*, and not a displacement-dependent, phenomenon.

The previously discussed possibility of the existence of both standing and running particle-wave modes also provides a probable explanation of the two types of emission if we identify the low-frequency pulses with standing waves and the continuous high-frequency emission with running waves. Then, the extent to which each type of emission takes place would indicate the proportion of lattice segments that are completely immobilized or pinned at the ends (at a given time), compared to others subject only to periodic changes in momentum.

In conclusion, we mention that the concentration of modes at the high-frequency end of the spectrum indicates that vibrations in the range 10^9–10^{10} cps might also occur during deformation. These frequencies are out of the range of the detection equipment used to monitor acoustic emission, however, and hence no conclusions about their existence can be drawn from the experimental work summarized here.

Conclusions

Results previously obtained for particle-momentum waves in infinite lattices have been modified to apply to finite lattice segments and to lattices with long-range periodicity (superstructure), such as might be expected in real crystals. Some of the consequences are:

(1) A series of discrete particle-wave frequencies or vibrational modes are found; these modes include both standing and running waves, where the frequency depends on Planck's constant, atomic mass, and segment length or atomic spacing.

(2) The frequency distribution function for these particle waves includes accumulations of modes at both the low- and high-frequency ends of the spectrum.

(3) From the considerable evidence for mosaic structures of the order of 10^{-4} cm in real crystals, closely spaced low-frequency modes in the audio range are predicted, along with an accumulation of modes at frequencies from 10^9 to 10^{10} cps dependent on the crystal spacing.

(4) Experimental evidence for the existence of non-elastic audio-frequency modes in crystals is in detailed qualitative agreement with expectations of the particle-wave view. In stretched natural rubber where a crystalline segment length is known from light scattering, calculated and measured values of the first standing-wave mode are 1040 and 1020 cps, respectively.

(5) The occurrence of non-elastic vibrations during unidirectional deformation of crystals is shown to result from the presence of net oscillating forces and torques acting on lattice segments during particle-wave propagation. Experimental evidence of acoustic emission during deformation is described and shown to be in general agreement with particle-wave ideas.

Audio-frequency mechanical resonances are thus adequately provided for in the particle-wave treatment of deformation, but it is not yet clear why such resonances should be as sharp as those found, nor why materials with widely different atomic masses often exhibit resonances of nearly the same frequency (e.g., ~ 3000 cps). Answers to these questions can be given only after the development of force–displacement and stress–strain laws for particle waves, and will be presented in the fourth chapter of this book. The reason for the prevalence of mosaic structures (and hence, segment lengths) of the order of 10^{-4} cm will also become evident later.

In the next chapter, characteristic velocities of deformation will be discussed and calculated for twenty cubic metals. An explanation of some hypervelocity effects will be offered and the concept of phonon fission advanced.

REFERENCES

1. A. J. Dekker, *Solid State Physics*, Prentice-Hall, Englewood Cliffs, N.J., 1957, Chap. 2.
2. M. Born and T. von Karman, *Physik. Z.*, **13**, 297–309 (1912); **14**, 15–19 (1913).
3. P. C. Fine, *Phys. Rev.*, **56**, 355–359 (1939).
4. M. Blackman, *Proc. Roy. Soc. (London)*, **A159**, 416–431 (1937).
5. R. B. Leighton, *Rev. Mod. Phys.*, **20**, 165–174 (1948).
6. E. W. Kellerman, *Phil. Trans. Roy. Soc. London*, **A238**, 513–548 (1940).
7. H. Smith, *Phil. Trans. Roy. Soc. London*, **A241**, 105–145 (1948).
8. See Appendix C.
9. C. G. Darwin, *Phil. Mag.*, **27**, 315–333; 675–690 (1914).
10. P. P. Ewald, *Ann. Phys.*, **54**, 519–556, 557–597 (1917).
11. C. G. Dunn and F. W. Daniels, *Trans. AIME*, **191**, 147–154 (1951).
12. R. D. Heidenreich, *J. Appl. Phys.*, **20**, 993–1010 (1949).
13. P. A. Beck and H. Hu, *Trans. AIME*, **185**, 627–634 (1949).
14. J. N. Kellar, P. B. Hirsch, and J. S. Thorp, *Nature*, **165**, 554–560 (1950).
15. C. S. Barrett, *Trans. AIME*, **156**, 62–81 (1944).
16. P. B. Hirsch, *Progr. Metal Phys.*, **6**, 236–339 (1956).
17. E. R. Fitzgerald, *Phys. Rev.*, **108**, 690–706 (1957); *J. Chem. Phys.*, **27**, 1180–1193 (1957); *J. Acoust. Soc. Am.*, **32**, 1270–1289 (1960).
18. E. R. Fitzgerald, *Phys. Rev.*, **112**, 1063–1075 (1958).
19. E. R. Fitzgerald, *J. Chem. Phys.*, **32**, 771–786 (1960).
20. E. R. Fitzgerald, in *Developments in Mechanics*, Vol. I, J. Lay and L. Malvern, Eds., Plenum Press, New York, 1961, pp. 10–38.
21. E. R. Fitzgerald, *Phys. Rev.*, **112**, 765–784 (1958).
22. E. R. Fitzgerald and M. T. Watson, *J. Acoust. Soc. Am.*, **32**, 584–593 (1960).
23. E. R. Fitzgerald, *J. Appl. Phys.*, **29**, 1442–1450 (1958).
24. E. R. Fitzgerald, unpublished data.
25. E. A. Hauser and H. Mark, *Kolloid-Beih.*, **22**, 63–73 (1926).
26. Goppel, results given by A. J. Wildschut, reference 28.
27. S. D. Gehman and J. E. Field, *J. Appl. Phys.*, **10**, 564–572 (1939).
28. A. J. Wildschut, *J. Appl. Phys.*, **17**, 51–60 (1946).
29. W. Yau and R. S. Stein, *J. Polymer Sci.*, **B2**, 231 (1964); *Bull. Am. Phys. Soc.*, **8**, 241 (1963); ONR Tech. Rept. No. 54 NR 356–378, August, 1963.
30. E. R. Fitzgerald, *J. Acoust. Soc. Am.*, **33**, 1305–1314 (1961).
31. E. R. Fitzgerald and A. E. Woodward, *Kolloid-Z.*, **172**, 177–181 (1960).
32. S. R. Bodner, *Trans. Soc. Rheol.*, **4**, 141–157 (1960).
33. E. R. Fitzgerald, *Phys. Letters*, **12**, 90–91 (1964).
34. E. R. Fitzgerald, *J. Acoust. Soc. Am.*, **36**, 2086–2089 (1964).

35. A. Portevin and F. Le Chatelier, *Compt. Rend.*, **176**, 507–510 (1923).
36. A. F. Joffé, *The Physics of Crystals*, McGraw-Hill, New York, 1928.
37. M. Klassen Nekludova, *Z. Physik.*, **55**, 555–568 (1929).
38. C. S. Barrett, *Structure of Metals*, McGraw-Hill, New York, 1952.
39. C. Crussard et al., *Compt. Rend.*, **246**, 2845–2848 (1958).
40. J. K. Redman, R. R. Coltman, and T. H. Blewitt, *J. Appl. Phys.*, **28**, 651–660 (1957).
41. J. Kaiser, *Arch. Eisenhuettenw.*, **50**, 43–54 (1953); *Forsch. Ing. Wes.*, **23** (1957).
42. B. H. Schofield, R. A. Bareiss, and A. A. Kyrala, *Acoustic Emission Under Applied Stress*, WADC Tech. Rept. 58–194 (ASTIA Document No. AD 155674), 1958; B. H. Schofield, *Acoustic Emission Under Applied Stress*, Aeronautical Research Laboratory Tech. Rept. ARL-150, 1961; B. H. Schofield, *Acoustic Emission Under Applied Stress*, *I*, Technical Documentary Report No. ASD-TDR-63-509, April, 1963; B. H. Schofield, *Acoustic Emission Under Applied Stress*, *II*, Technical Documentary Report No. ASD-TDR-63-509, May, 1964.
43. C. A. Tatro, private communication.
44. J. P. Cusick, *Bull. Am. Phys. Soc.*, **8**, 237 (1963).
45. R. G. Liptai and C. A. Tatro, *Metallurgical Society Program*, October 20, 1964, p. 12.
46. J. Powers and V. Valkenburg, *Bull. Am. Phys. Soc.*, **8**, 243 (1963); J. Powers, private communication.

HIGH-VELOCITY DEFORMATION AND IMPACT

Introduction

In preceding chapters, consideration has been given to the propagation of associated particle waves in solids. These waves were supposed to arise from internal field-free particles moving with velocities up to a limit, v_1, determined by the lattice spacing. The values of these limiting velocities are low—well below the speed of sound, in fact—and the occurrence of non-elastic deformations at much higher velocities is well known.[1] The question naturally arises then as to the usefulness of the particle-wave viewpoint in explaining high-speed deformation. Are we to expect that such deformations proceed by an altogether different process? Or is there some means by which the particle waves can, after all, be generated by free particles with velocities above $v_1 = h/2md_1$, and yet be propagated through a crystal lattice?

1. The Effect of Lattice Motion

The results obtained so far have been in terms of a fixed or stationary lattice. Therefore, the possibility exists that the results might be modified if a crystal lattice, or parts of it, move with respect to the system of laboratory coordinates in which the free-particle velocity is measured. We let v_t be the velocity of translation of the lattice with fixed spacing, d_1, along the incident direction and v_i be the velocity of an incident field-free particle, as indicated schematically in Figure 3.1. The distance moved by the field-free particle in reaching the lattice can be expressed in terms of the lattice spacing as pd_1, in accordance with previous notation. Then the time required for the field-free particle to travel up to a stationary lattice is

$$t = pd_1/v_i \tag{3.1}$$

while for a lattice section moving toward the incident free particle with velocity, v_ℓ, this time is reduced to

$$t' = (p\boldsymbol{d}_1 - v_\ell t')/v_i \qquad (3.2)$$

$$= p\boldsymbol{d}_1'/v_i \qquad (3.2')$$

where a new, apparent spacing, $\boldsymbol{d}_1'$, is defined by

$$p\boldsymbol{d}_1' = p\boldsymbol{d}_1 - v_\ell t' \qquad (3.3)$$

Equation 3.2 may be solved for t' to give

$$t' = p\boldsymbol{d}_1/(v_i + v_\ell) \qquad (3.4)$$

and by forming the ratio $t'/t = \boldsymbol{d}_1'/\boldsymbol{d}_1$ from Eqs. 3.1, 3.2', and 3.4, we get the value of the apparent spacing $\boldsymbol{d}_1'$ as

$$\boldsymbol{d}_1' \text{ (contracted)} = \boldsymbol{d}_1 \frac{v_i}{v_i + v_\ell} \qquad (3.5)$$

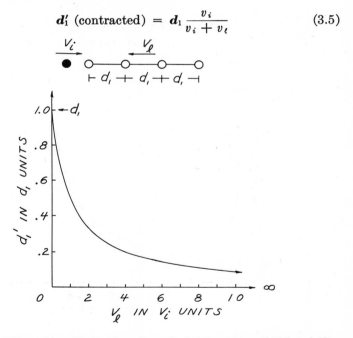

Fig. 3.1. Effect of translational motion of a lattice segment with velocity, v_ℓ, on the apparent lattice spacing, $\boldsymbol{d}_1'$, seen by an incident free particle (with velocity, v_i) for the lattice moving *toward* the incident particle.

This variation of d_1' with lattice velocity is shown in Figure 3.1. The apparent spacing clearly decreases as the lattice moves toward the incident particle with increasing velocity.

In an entirely similar way, it can be demonstrated that, for a lattice moving *away* from the incident particle, the apparent spacing, d_1'', increases with lattice velocity according to

$$d_1'' \text{ (extended)} = d_1 \frac{v_i}{v_i - v_\ell} \tag{3.6}$$

and as shown in Figure 3.2. Eqs. 3.5 and 3.6 can be combined into a single expression

$$d_{1\,i}' \text{ (apparent)} = d_1 \frac{v_i}{v_i \pm v_\ell} \tag{3.7}$$

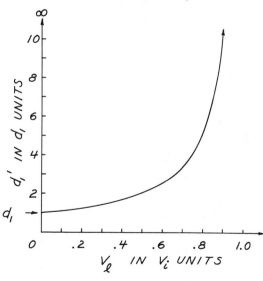

Fig. 3.2. Effect of translational motion of a lattice segment with velocity, v_ℓ, on the apparent lattice spacing, d_1', seen by an incident free particle (with velocity, v_i) for the lattice moving *away from* the incident particle.

where positive values of v_ℓ denote lattice motion *toward* the incident field-free particle and negative values indicate lattice motion *away* *from* the incoming particle.

From Eq. 3.7 it is possible to calculate a new value of limiting free-particle velocity, v_1', according to

$$v_1' = \frac{h}{2m \boldsymbol{d_1'}} \tag{3.8}$$

where $\boldsymbol{d_1'}$ is the value of $\boldsymbol{d_{1i}}$ for $v_i = v_1'$

or

$$v_1' = v_1 \frac{v_1' \pm v_\ell}{v_1'} \tag{3.9}$$

From Eq. 3.9 it is evident that free-particle velocities greatly in excess of those calculated for a stationary lattice can cause propagation of particle waves for a lattice moving toward the incoming free particle. The velocities are, in fact, restricted only by whatever limits may prevail for the speed of the lattice motion.

2. DEVELOPMENT OF REVERSED LATTICE MOTION

In considering the effect of lattice motion on the ability of an incident particle and its associated particle wave to travel through a lattice, the question naturally arises: How are reversed lattice velocities created? In order to investigate this process, it is convenient to consider the limiting, incident free-particle velocity, v_1', as the given or independent variable, and then determine necessary values of lattice velocity, v_ℓ, as a function of v_1'. The behavior of the lattice atoms for free-particle impact at velocities v_1' can be seen from Eq. 3.9 if it is solved for v_ℓ,

$$v_\ell = v_1'(1 - v_1'/v_1) \tag{3.10}$$

and where *negative* values of v_ℓ now indicate velocities opposite to the incident particle velocity, v_1', taken as reference. A plot of v_ℓ as a function of limiting incident, free-particle velocity, v_1', is then an inverted parabola with vertex at $(v_1/2, v_1/4)$, as shown in Figure 3.3.

From this curve, it is clear that at incident velocities above v_1 the lattice must move with negative velocities (in a direction reverse to that of the incident particle) of increasing magnitude, in order to allow propagation of the incident particle wave. The curve of Figure 3.3 gives the mathematical conditions for the type of motion supposed to take place, but a physical source for momentum reversal and the actual increase in total momentum and energy at velocities above $2v_1$ must also be present. It is evident that this source can be only the vibrational (phonon) momentum and energy of the crystal lattice itself. In fact, as we shall see later, the process eventually results in destruction of the crystal lattice when the free-particle impact

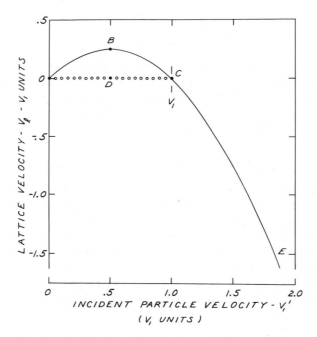

Fig. 3.3. Translational lattice velocity, v_ℓ, needed to provide an apparent lattice spacing for which the incident free-particle velocity, v_1', will be the limiting velocity for particle-wave propagation in the lattice (branch OBC). Discrete values of v_1' below v_1 also occur for $v_\ell = 0$, as indicated by the points along the abscissae (branch ODC). Above v_1, lattice segments must move *against* the incoming particle according to the single, negative branch, CE.

velocity is such as to demand an increase in energy equal to the binding energy of the lattice.

Before further discussion of reverse lattice motion at free-particle velocities above v_1, something must be said about the positive branch of the parabola of Figure 3.3 and forward lattice motion below v_1. According to our previous remarks, it is not necessary for *any* lattice motion to occur for free-particle velocities below v_1. All particle waves generated at velocities below v_1 are propagated in an infinite lattice, and a series of waves at discrete wave lengths are propagated in a finite lattice. In the latter case, if the segment length is $S = N\boldsymbol{d}_1$, the allowed values of wave vector, k, are discrete, leading to discrete values of incident free-particle velocities according to $v_i = \hbar k/m$ and,

$$v_{iq} = \frac{\hbar}{m} \frac{q\pi}{N\boldsymbol{d}_1} \tag{3.11}$$

$$= v_1 \frac{q}{N} \tag{3.11'}$$

$$q = 1, 2, 3 \ldots (N - 1)$$

where

$$v_1 = h/2m\boldsymbol{d}_1$$

Then there will be a series of evenly spaced allowed velocities along the abscissa ($v_\ell = 0$) between 0 and v_1, as indicated in Figure 3.3, (branch ODC), as well as the continuous values for forward lattice motion according to the positive branch (OBC) of the curve. Hence, there appears to be a choice of lattice behavior for free-particle velocities below v_1: (*1*) the lattice remains stationary and propagates particle waves only of certain discrete wavelengths; or (*2*) the lattice moves forward at varying velocities, v_ℓ, given by Eq. 3.10, and propagates particle waves of continuous wavelengths between 0 and $2\boldsymbol{d}_1$. Above v_1, there is only one possibility, i.e., the lattice must reverse and move *against* an incident free particle to allow particle-wave propagation for wavelengths less than $2\boldsymbol{d}_1$.

The conditions under which the lattice moves (*1*) or remains stationary (*2*) for free-particle velocities below v_1 will presently be shown to represent the difference between transient and equilibrium behavior, respectively.

In the meantime, it will be convenient to distinguish between three distinct types of energy in considering free-particle impact against a crystal lattice: (1) the kinetic energy of the incoming field-free particle, U_i; (2) the translational kinetic energy of a lattice mass (atom), U_ℓ, which may result from motion of the lattice or a section of the lattice; and (3) the change in vibrational energy of the lattice atoms (phonons), ΔU_v. This last energy is attributed to the presence in a crystal of quantized vibrational modes or sound particles called phonons, in a manner which will be described in detail later. For lattice atoms of mass m, the absolute value of v_ℓ will be a measure of the translational energy per mass (atom) according to

$$| v_\ell | = \sqrt{2U_\ell/m} \tag{3.12}$$

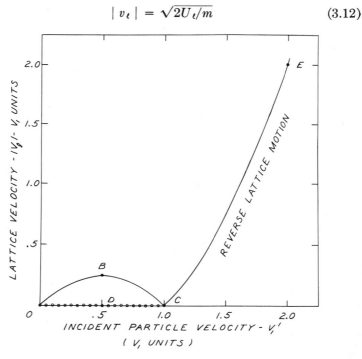

Fig. 3.4. Absolute value of translational lattice velocity $| v_\ell |$ vs. limiting incident free-particle velocity, v_1', to maintain necessary apparent spacing for propagation of limiting particle waves, as in Figure 3.3. Lattice moves against incident particle direction above $v_1 = h/2md_1$, where d_1 is lattice spacing in slip direction, m is particle mass, and h is Planck's constant.

and if a curve of $|v_\ell|$ vs. v_1' is drawn as shown in Figure 3.4, the practical result is that the negative branch above v_1 is reflected upward. This curve, in effect, now becomes an energy–velocity relation which must hold if deformation is to take place by the particle-wave process. It remains to be seen whether other conditions are, in fact, compatible with those shown in Figure 3.4.

3. Momentum Conditions

To fix operating points on the $|v_\ell|$ vs. v_1' curve of Figure 3.4, we require conservation of momentum in the particle–lattice system. The momentum of an incoming particle is transferred entirely to the lattice after collision. That is, before entering the lattice, the particle has momentum, but after exists only as a standing wave in the lattice with zero net momentum. The lattice in turn experiences a change in phonon momentum, ΔP_v, and gains a translational lattice momentum. We must also ask how many lattice particles, n, can be expected to share in the momentum transferred by a single incoming particle? Since the apparent lattice spacing varies to "fit" the incoming particle wavelength, $\lambda' = 2d_1'$, at *least two* lattice masses must move together to define the new spacing, d_1'. However, it is possible that three or more might really participate. Further, the change in phonon momentum might extend to more or fewer atoms than those acquiring translational motion. For just two lattice masses the situation is as shown below:

	Momentum	
	Before impact	After impact
Incoming particle	mv_1'	0
Crystal lattice (2 atoms)	P_v'	$P_v \pm 2mv_\ell$

Hence,

$$mv_1' = \Delta P_v \pm 2mv_\ell$$

where

$$\Delta P_v = P_v - P_v'$$

or

$$| v_\ell | = \Delta P_v/2m - v_1'/2 \qquad \text{(two lattice atoms)} \qquad (3.13)$$

$$| v_\ell | = \Delta P_v/nm - v_1'/n \qquad \text{(n lattice atoms)} \qquad (3.14)$$

The momentum condition of Eq. 3.13 can be used as a "load line" to obtain[2] operating points on the upper branch (OBC) of the characteristic $|v_\ell|$ vs. v_1' curve, as shown in Figure 3.5. In general, families of lines of slope $-1/n$ will be obtained which move across the figure as a function of $\Delta P_v/nm$. The intersection of such a momentum line with any point on the characteristic curve defines a value of $|v_\ell|$ for the corresponding value of impact velocity, v_1'. Consider, for example, the set of momentum lines AD of slope $-1/2$, shown in Figure 3.5. As the momentum change of the crystal phonons increases, this line moves across the figure with intersection A', A'' with the branch OB of the characteristic curve. When this intersection reaches the point S, any further slight increase in ΔP_v will result in a sudden jump to S' on the reversed lattice curve CE, with a drop in $|v_\ell|$ (hence, a decrease in translational lattice energy) and a reversal of lattice velocity. Points between S and C on branch BC are unstable, so that erratic jumps or oscillations can be expected for impact velocities between $0.50v_1$ and $0.75v_1$ and between about v_1 to $1.05v_1$ for a line of slope $-1/2$.

The exact location of the instability point, S, will depend on the number of lattice atoms sharing the translational energy at any time. This number will increase as the particle wave travels through the lattice after impact (at velocities below v_1) and the point, S, will approach $0.5v_1$ as the number of participating atoms increases to a large value. Evidently, S will occur at incident velocities between $0.75v_1$ and $0.5v_1$. The preceding analysis is similar to that used in discussing the theory of electronic trigger circuits.

From these momentum considerations, it is possible to explain the existence of two branches in the $|v_\ell|$ vs. v_1' curve in terms of the number of lattice masses, n, among which the free-particle momentum is shared after impact, and consequently, in terms of the time after impact. To see how this is done, we notice that the slope of the momentum line will approach zero as the number of lattice masses, n, sharing the free-particle momentum increases to a large number. At the same time, the intercept $\Delta Pv/nm$ also becomes small so that the

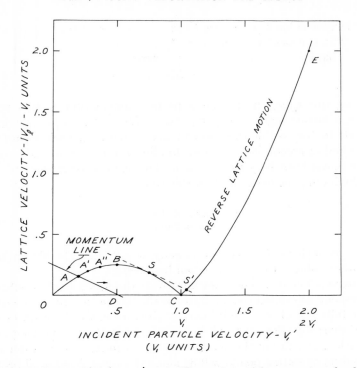

Fig. 3.5. Curve of $|\,v_\ell\,|$ vs. v_1', as in Figure 3.4, with momentum load line added according to Eq. 3.13 of text, where $n = 2$. Intersections of momentum line with $|\,v_\ell\,|$ vs. v_1' curve (e.g., A, A', A'', etc.) give possible "operating" points.

momentum line will eventually lie along (or very near) the abscissa of the $|v_\ell|$ vs. v_1' curve and intersect the discrete allowed values of v_{iq} along the lower branch (ODC) of the characteristic curve. The time necessary for the momentum of a single incoming particle to be spread among a large number, N, of lattice atoms can be estimated from the group velocity of the particle wave which carries the momentum through the lattice. An expression for this group velocity was given in the first chapter of this book, but can be rewritten in terms of the incident free-particle velocity, v_i as

$$v_g \,(\text{particle}) \;=\; \frac{2}{\pi}\, v_1 \sin\left(\frac{\pi}{2}\frac{v_i}{v_1}\right) \cos\left(\frac{\pi}{2}\frac{v_i}{v_1}\right) \qquad (3.15)$$

The largest value of v_g occurs when $v_i = v_1/2$, and then v_g (max) $= v_1/\pi$. The transient behavior time of a lattice is

$$t \geq 2S\pi/v_1 \tag{3.16}$$

During this time, the incoming particle momentum is distributed along a lattice segment of length $S = Nd_1$ as the incoming wave travels to the end of the segment and is reflected back again; the slope and intercept of the momentum line approach zero and steady-state (lower branch) behavior sets in. For segment lengths of 10^{-4} cm in aluminum, the *lower* limit on this time is

$$t \geq 0.25 \times 10^{-6} \text{ sec}$$
$$\text{(aluminum)}$$

when the incident free-particle velocity is $v_1/2$ (1.292×10^3 cm/sec). At other values of v_i, the time will be longer.

Intersections of momentum lines with the upper branch actually correspond to excited energy states of the lattice, as will be described more fully elsewhere.[3] Under normal circumstances, these states will be of short duration; through loss of energy to the surroundings, the vibrational energy of the crystal will return to its original value and long-term operating points will lie along the lower, horizontal branch of the $|v_t|$ vs. v_i' curve.

4. Characteristic Deformation Velocities

As a result of the discussion so far, it is possible to predict the initial response of a crystal lattice as a function of impact velocity. First, there will be a range of velocities between $v_1/2$ and $3v_1/4$ in which oscillations or other evidence of erratic behavior occur. Second, at impact velocities above v_1, the lattice atoms move against the incoming particle. This reverse motion will result in severe local distortion of the lattice and the beginning of "reverse-flow" deformation. Because of the instability conditions above $v_1/2$, as a practical matter, such reverse flow will start at some point S beyond $v_1/2$; that is, any incoming particle with a velocity between that at S and v_1 will sooner or later jump to a velocity just above v_1, as previously described, and the lattice will then move in the reverse direction. The extra energy is supplied to the particle by the crystal lattice, since the point above v_1 corresponds to lower $|v_t|$ and energy than the point at S. Third, above velocity $2v_1$, the reverse flow will become unusually severe as the lattice atoms move in the reverse direction, at velocities above that of the incident particle, and with energy which must in some way be supplied by the crystal itself.

The translational velocity demanded of each lattice atom will eventually reach a final value, v_{tf}, such that the energy required of each lattice atom equals the dissociation energy per atom, D, of the crystal lattice. If v_f is the incident particle velocity which requires the final translational lattice velocity, v_{tf}, then by substituting in Eq. 3.9 for reversed lattice motion, we get

$$v_1' \text{ (final)} = v_f = \frac{v_1 + \sqrt{v_1{}^2 + 4v_1 v_{tf}}}{2} \tag{3.17}$$

or

$$v_f = \frac{v_1}{2} (1 + \sqrt{1 + 4v_{tf}/v_1}) \tag{3.17'}$$

If $v_{tf} \gg v_1$ and $2\sqrt{v_{tf}/v_1} \gg 1$, then Eq. 3.17' can be reduced to the approximation

$$v_f \cong \sqrt{v_1 v_{tf}} \tag{3.18}$$

which is accurate to within 5% if $v_{tf}/v_1 \geq 100$. Since v_1 is the limiting velocity for the stationary lattice given by $h/2md_1$, a value for the velocity, v_f, necessary to produce lattice disintegration or fracture can be calculated if v_{tf} is determined.

From these comments, we expect that the macroscopic deformation of crystals may turn out to be closely connected with certain internal characteristic velocities: v_1, $2v_1$, and v_f. For example, in compression-impact tests between cylindrical samples of the same diameter, a result of reversed lattice motion should be an outward or radial spreading as the reversed lattice particles pile up against the impact faces of the samples. This flaring out should start first at the impact face of the samples, reach its largest value there, and decrease with distance into the samples. Conversely, in tension impact above v_1, lattice atoms will move away from the outward, moving end of a specimen and produce an inward contraction or "necking down." While these flaring or necking effects occur at internal velocities above v_1, they may appear to commence at impact velocities anywhere between $v_1/2$ and $3v_1/4$ because of the instabilities previously outlined. Both the flaring and necking must be sharply increased at velocities above $2v_1$, and fracture or lattice disintegration will occur for velocities above v_f.

5. Release of Lattice Energy—Phonon Fission

In obtaining an expression for the final incident velocity, v_f, above which fracture or disintegration of a lattice will occur, an ultimate or final translational velocity, v_{tf}, for the lattice atoms themselves was described above which the lattice was expected to break up. This velocity, v_{tf}, can be related to the dissociation energy per atom, D, of the crystal lattice in the following manner: Let the heat energy necessary to change a solid sample of mass M into a gas or vapor be equal to U. The solid sample originally consisted of some number of atoms, n, (equal to M/m, where m is the mass of each atom) held together by cohesive or binding forces between the atoms. In the vapor state these strong solid-state attractions between atoms are entirely missing; individual atoms in the gaseous state interact or attract one another only very weakly, if at all. Hence, the total energy required to first melt and then vaporize the solid, divided by the number of atoms present, gives a measure of the cohesive energy or binding energy per atom in the solid

$$D = U/n \tag{3.19}$$

This ratio is evidently equal to the energy per atom needed to cause dissociation of the atoms in a solid, and thus is also the required dissociation energy per atom.

If, instead of melting a solid sample, we imagine it to be taken apart by pulling apart the atoms, then the energy needed to remove or "dissociate" each atom from the lattice will again be, on the average, equal to D. On the other hand, if a crystal lattice is broken up into n-atom chunks instead of single atoms, only a fraction of the former total energy is needed, so that the dissociation energy *per atom* will be reduced. In a one-dimensional row lattice, for example, dissociation into two-atom segments will require a dissociation energy *per atom* of only $D/2$, instead of D; in a two-dimensional lattice, a break up into four-atom squares will likewise require only an energy of $D/2$ per atom; and a three-dimensional lattice can be broken into eight-atom cubes with a dissociation energy of $D/2$ per atom. This is illustrated for one- and three-dimensional lattices in Figure 3.6. Returning now to the case where an incident free particle strikes a row lattice at a velocity above v_1, we recognize that a two-atom lattice segment required to move against the incoming particle direction with velocity v_{tf} will have sufficient energy to break loose from the lattice if the required translational energy of each atom is $\frac{1}{2}mv_{tf}^2$, where

$$\frac{1}{2} mv_{tf}^2 = D/2 \tag{3.20}$$

or

$$v_{tf} = \sqrt{D/m} \tag{3.20'}$$

and D is the dissociation energy per atom for the lattice (cohesive energy per atom). In the same way, a four-atom "projectile" incident

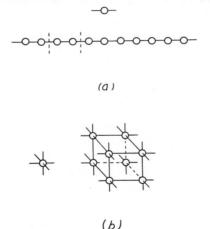

(a)

(b)

Fig. 3.6. (*a*) Schematic representation of the reduction in dissociation energy per atom required to break up a row lattice into two-atom segments instead of single atoms. Reduction results because fewer "bonds" per atom are broken to form the two-atom segments. (*b*) Schematic representation of the reduction in dissociation energy per atom required to break up a three-dimensional lattice into eight-atom chunks instead of single atoms. Reduction again results because fewer "bonds" per atom are broken to form the eight-atom chunks.

on a three-dimensional crystal will break off an eight-atom cube if the two-atom segments opposite the projectile atoms are again required to move at velocities of $v_{\ell f}$ (given by Eq. 3.20') against the incoming projectile. These ideas are represented schematically in Figure 3.7. Of course, a single atom incident on a three-dimensional lattice can also cause ejection of two-atom segments when the incident velocity, v_f', is such as to require a lattice velocity, $v_{\ell f}'$, where

$$v_{\ell f}' = \sqrt{5D/3m} \qquad (3.21)$$

instead of a velocity $v_{\ell f} = \sqrt{D/m}$ required by v_f. With macroscopic projectiles, however, disintegration of the target crystal will always begin at the lower incident velocity.

From Eqs. 3.20' and 3.17' (or 3.18), it is now clearly possible to calculate and predict an incident projectile velocity, v_f, at which a target crystal will begin to disintegrate or break up if values of the dissociation energy per atom, D, are known. Values of D can be ob-

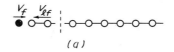

(a)

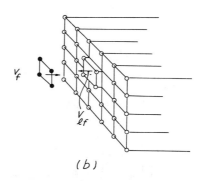

(b)

Fig. 3.7. (a) Diagram showing how two-atom segments of a row lattice break off to move against an incident particle with velocity, v_f, when the required reversed lattice velocity, $v_{\ell f}$, equals $\sqrt{D/m}$, where D is the dissociation energy per atom and m is the mass of the lattice atoms. (b) Diagram showing how an eight-atom piece of a crystal lattice breaks off to move against an incident four-atom "projectile" with velocity v_f requiring a reversed lattice velocity, $v_{\ell f} = \sqrt{D/m}$, as discussed in the text.

tained, in principal, from careful thermal measurements in which the total heat energy needed to vaporize a solid is measured. For high-melting solids, such as some of the metals, these measurements are extremely difficult to carry out with accuracy; wide variations in reported values of D often occur; but, on the other hand, the velocity, v_f, is dependent on the fourth root of D, so that uncertainties in velocities will be about one-fourth those in measured values of D.

It is possible to calculate v_f more precisely by introducing the concept of phonon fission[4] and using measured values of elastic (sound) wave velocities. We recall, as mentioned previously, that it is possible to show that the discrete vibrational elastic-wave modes of a crystal lattice are equivalent to an array of quantized harmonic oscillators. The average energy of each vibrational mode of frequency v_e of a lattice atom is then given by

$$<U_k> = \frac{h\nu_e}{2} + \frac{h\nu_e}{e^{h\nu_e/kT} - 1}\qquad(3.22)$$

With each vibrational elastic mode we can associate a certain number of quanta, n_k, where $h\nu_e$ is the energy of each. Then

$$n_k = <U_k>/h\nu_e \qquad(3.23)$$

and the quanta, n_k, can be thought of as sound particles or phonons (by analogy with light particles or photons), as already mentioned. From Eq. 3.22, vibrational energy exists in the lattice even at absolute zero; that is, there is an intrinsic vibrational energy associated with a crystal quite apart from thermal vibrations. This zero-point vibration suggests that there are also certain irreducible or intrinsic (non-thermal) phonons associated with the atoms in a crystal lattice. Two-atom lattice combinations, such as those shown in Figure 3.8, will consist of two transverse phonons, one longitudinal phonon, and have a mass, m. This same result is obtained from Eqs. 3.22 and 3.23 by noting that one longitudinal and two transverse vibrational modes can be associated with each atom in a crystal, yielding a total of three phonons for two atoms at $T = 0°K$.

Each time an atom breaks loose from a lattice, three phonons of the type depicted in Figure 3.8 are destroyed. The disappearance or

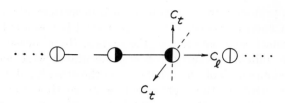

Fig. 3.8. Diagram showing how two transverse phonons (velocity, c_t) and one longitudinal phonon (velocity, c_ℓ) can be associated with any two-atom combination in a crystal lattice. Each atom in the combination contributes a mass, $m/2$, to the isolated vibrational mode depicted, so that the total phonon mass of the two-atom system is m.

annihilation of these phonons might be expected to result in a release of energy equal to $m\bar{c}_s^2$, where $\bar{c}_s$ is a mean sound velocity for the one longitudinal and two transverse phonons according to

$$\bar{c}_s^2 = \frac{2c_t^2 + c_\ell^2}{3} \tag{3.24}$$

$$\bar{c}_s = c_t \sqrt{\frac{2 + (c_\ell/c_t)^2}{3}} \tag{3.25}$$

The energy released per atom will be $m\bar{c}_s^2/2$, or mc_s^2 if $c_s = \bar{c}_s/\sqrt{2}$. In vaporizing a solid by supplying heat energy, the final result is also the destruction of all intrinsic lattice phonons where the separated atoms each have an energy equal to D (per atom) above their original energy in the lattice. Hence, it seems reasonable to consider that the destruction of intrinsic lattice phonons will always be accompanied by the energy, D, for each separated atom

$$D = mc_s^2 \tag{3.26}$$

where

$$c_s^2 = (2c_t^2 + c_\ell^2)/6 \tag{3.27}$$

and c_t, c_ℓ, are the transverse and longitudinal sound velocities, respectively, in the solid.

The form of Eq. 3.26 is suggested also by analogy with the relation between energy, mass, and light velocity, c, from Einstein's special theory of relativity

$$E = mc^2 \tag{3.28}$$

In general, the expression for the mean sound velocity c_s will depend upon three orthogonal sets of longitudinal and transverse sound velocities, i.e., a general crystal lattice can be characterized by a minimum of three longitudinal phonons and six transverse phonons. However, for cubic crystals only three phonons (one longitudinal and two transverse) are needed because of symmetry.

A comparison of values of $\sqrt{D/m}$ with values of c_s calculated from measured sound velocities is presented for 18 fcc and bcc metals in Table 3.1. The agreement is good considering that values of D are not too reliable, as already mentioned. By comparing Eqs. 3.20' and 3.26, it is evident that $v_{tf} = c_s$, so that the incident particle velocity, v_f, producing disintegration of a lattice will be

$$v_f \cong \sqrt{v_1 \cdot c_s} \tag{3.29}$$

We can now refer to this as the phonon-fission velocity, since an incident particle at this velocity will cause the lattice to break up and produce phonon splitting or fission. Values of v_1 are of the order of 10^2 to 10^3 cm/sec, while c_s is generally about 10^5 cm/sec. Therefore, v_f will be from 10^3 to 10^4 cm/sec, and the energy required for the incident particle to produce fission is less than one-hundredth of that released for lattice particles of the same mass

$$\frac{m}{2} v_f^2 \leq 0.01 \ mc_s^2$$

so that *self-sustained fission* is possible if fragments of the fissioned lattice in turn strike other lattice sections and produce more fission, etc.

The explosive nature of certain fractures may arise from this source.

6. SOME EXPERIMENTAL RESULTS

Of all the consequences flowing from the particle-wave view of deformation, the most bizarre, in terms of usual ideas, is that of reversed

TABLE 3.1

Characteristic Deformation Velocities for Some Cubic Metals and Verification of the Relation[a]

$$D = mc_s^2 \text{ or } c_s = \sqrt{D/m}$$

Metal	m Atomic mass 10^{-23} g	d_1 Spacing in slip direction 10^{-8} cm	v_1 $h/2md_1$ 10^3 cm/sec	v_f Velocity for fission 10^4 cm/sec	D Lattice dissociation energy ev/atom	$\sqrt{\dfrac{D}{m}}$ 10^5 cm/sec	c_s Observed mean sound velocity[b] 10^5 cm/sec
Al	4.48	2.86_2	2.58_5	2.92	3.21	3.3_6	3.19
Ni[c]	9.74	2.49_1	1.36_4	2.26	4.94	2.8_5	3.05
Cu	10.55	2.55_6	1.22_9	1.89	4.11	2.5_0	2.45
Sr	14.55	4.31	.528	.85	1.69	1.3_7	—
Pd	17.66	2.75_0	.682	1.29	4.28	2.0_7	2.26
Ag	17.89	2.88_8	$.641_0$	1.14	3.18	1.7_8	1.81
Pt	32.38	2.77_5	$.368_6$	.776	6.45	1.7_8	1.90
Au	32.70	2.88_4	$.351_2$	.720	4.67	1.5_1	1.52
Pb	34.39	3.49_9	$.275_3$	.559	2.38	1.0_5	1.05
Th	38.51	3.60	$.238_9$	.695	5.92	1.5_7	1.56

Li	1.15	3.03_9	9.46_2	6.55	1.60	4.6_9	—
Na	3.82	3.71_5	2.33_6	2.20	1.13	2.1_7	1.93
K	6.49	4.62_7	1.10_3	1.39	0.954	1.5_4	1.33
V	8.45	2.63_2	1.48_8	2.12	5.20	3.1_4	3.04
Cr[c]	8.65	2.49_8	1.53_6	2.49	4.24	2.8_1	3.42
Fe[e]	9.27	2.48_1	1.44_0	2.36	4.21	2.7_0	3.10
Mo	10.59	2.72_5	$.763_1$	1.67	8.67	3.6_2	3.54
Nb	15.40	2.85_9	$.751_0$	1.39	7.59	2.7_9	2.64
Ta	30.00	2.86_0	$.385_0$	.920	8.02	2.0_7	2.08
W	30.45	2.73_9	$.396_2$	1.05	10.3	2.3_4	2.63

[a] Values of D taken as the heat of vaporization at room temperature from National Nuclear Energy Series, Vol. 19B, *The Chemistry and Metallurgy of Miscellaneous Materials*, L. L. Quill, McGraw-Hill, New York, 1950, pp. 26–27; and *Metallurgical Problems*, A. Butts, McGraw-Hill, New York, 1943, pp. 391–392. Considerable variation exists in D as given by different sources; the values of c_s are probably more reliable. Values of c_l and c_t (used to calculate c_s) from an article by H. B. Huntington in *Solid State Phys.*, **7**, 274 (1958), and the following journal references: *J. Appl. Phys.*, **32**, 100 (1961); **33**, 3266 (1962); **33**, 2311 (1962); **30**, 36 (1959); *Phys. Rev.*, **129**, 1063 (1963); **122**, 1714 (1961); **119**, 1532 (1960); **119**, 1246 (1960); **118**, 1545 (1960).

[b] Calculated according to $c_s = \sqrt{(2c_i^2 + c_l^2)/6}$ as discussed in the text.

[c] Values depend strongly on the magnetic state of the sample, and various crystal transitions occur before the melting point is reached.

lattice motion. In classical elastic collision theories, for example, we cannot imagine a target initially at rest moving *toward* a projectile as a result of a collision; we all "know" the target will, if it moves at all, move with or in the same direction as the incident projectile.

Now, in terms of particle waves, we have concluded that above a certain characteristic velocity, v_1, the target (or at least sections of it) will tend to move toward an incoming projectile and, even more strangely, that at velocities above still another characteristic value, v_f, the target will actually disintegrate or break up; sections of the target will fly off *against* the incident projectile. Furthermore, we do not suppose that the reversed motion stems from any rebounds or reflections from some depth (or back surface) within the sample. On the contrary, above v_f, sections of the target in the impact area should peel off from the surface in groups of two atoms or so at a time. It is an important part of the idea that the fragments breaking off retain the original lattice spacing within themselves, and therefore, that the process is not one of melting or increasing disorder within lattice sections. In fact, from our point of view, the disintegrations should be *crystallographic*, i.e., the lattice sections will fly off in slip directions in which maximum momentum transfer can take place.

For experimental verification of these ideas, we turn first to high-velocity collisions or hypervelocity impact tests. A number of investigations of the effects of small projectiles impinging at high speeds on large (semi-infinite) targets have been reported. One of the principal results of hypervelocity impact is crater formation in the target, with a loss of target material and often the complete disappearance, i.e., "vaporization" of the projectile. Small spheres of polycrystalline lead, tin, iron, aluminum, zinc, and silver were impacted at velocities from 0.75×10^5 to 2.25×10^5 cm/sec into large targets of the same material by Partridge, Vanfleet, and Whited.[5] They found that hemispherical craters of much larger diameter than the spheres were formed where the depth of the crater (penetration) increased with pellet velocity above a certain threshold or "critical" velocity. Valkenburg et al.[6] have reported similar experiments where 1/8-in. diameter spherical pellets were shot into semi-infinite targets. Metals used included polycrystalline aluminum, magnesium, steel, brass, lead, and zinc. Large craters roughly hemispherical in shape were again formed, with a projection of material (petalling) around the lip of the crater in many instances. The targets were carefully weighed before and after impact, and a net loss of weight was observed; this was attributed to a breaking off of some of the petals of metal around the crater lip. No traces of the pellets were found in the craters at the velocities used (1–5 $\times$ 10^5 cm/sec). The penetrations of projectiles into the targets again increased with incident pellet velocity, as did the size (volume) of the craters formed. Photographs of target cross sections showing some typical crater profiles[7] are adduced in Figures 3.9 and 3.10. Crater formation in lead targets by spherical iron pellets with radii less than 2 $\times$ 10^{-4} cm has been studied by Friichtenicht

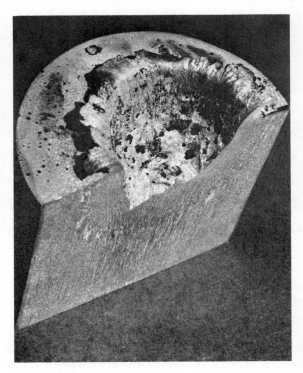

Fig. 3.9. Photograph of a crater formed in a dead annealed 2S aluminum block by a 1.122-gram type-1020 steel pellet incident at 4.00 $\times$ 10^5 cm/sec. After impact the block was cut in half and etched to show crystallographic effects extending into the block under the crater, as shown in Figure 3.10. Before impact the aluminum consisted of very small, randomly oriented grains. (Specimen furnished by courtesy of Prof. R. B. Pond, The Johns Hopkins University.)

Fig. 3.10. Photograph of the side of the sectioned block of Figure 3.9.

and Hameresh[8] with impact velocities up to 1.7×10^5 cm/sec. Microscopic craters of the same general type as found for larger projectiles were obtained. These had diameters of 3 to 4×10^{-4} cm for projectile diameters of about 0.5×10^{-4} cm, for example. Measurements of both velocity and crater size were necessarily less precise in these experiments, but, in general, the size of the craters increased with impact velocity. Somewhat larger microparticles with diameters in the range from 10^{-3} to 10^{-2} cm were used in hypervelocity-impact experiments reported by Gehring and Richards[9] at velocities of about 10^6 cm/sec. More than twenty different target materials were used, and hemispherical craters were found after impact. Hypervelocity impact in lead has been studied by Clark et al.,[10] and in aluminum, cadmium, copper, lead, and zinc by Kineke.[11] In the latter case, steel pellets with masses from 0.18 to 8.86 grams and velocities in the range from 2 to 5×10^5 cm/sec were fired into semi-infinite targets. The results were similar to those already described. Hypervelocity-penetration results of the same general type have also been reported by many others.

From our point of view, we are most interested in three aspects of the phenomena. First, the crater appearance indicates that target material has moved out away from the target face toward the incoming projectile; and then the dual result that the crater is much larger than the projectile and that a loss of material from the target occurs. These characteristics are in agreement with the concepts of lattice reversal and eventual phonon fission as previously discussed. The shape of the crater, and especially the crater lip, has in the past led to the idea that some melting occurs in hypervelocity impact by comparison with the splashing or instantaneous craters produced in a liquid when a liquid drop meets a liquid surface. Such liquid–liquid impacts were studied first by Worthington[12] (1897, 1908) and more recently by Engel.[13] However, the particle-wave approach rejects such a view of cratering in solids; the material ejected from the target may be perhaps in a fairly dispersed form, but each small particle will retain its crystallographic integrity. As made clear in the original discussion, the crystal sections may range in size down to pieces of only two or three lattice spacings ($6–10 \times 10^{-8}$ cm), however. Perhaps the most direct confirmation of the particle-wave view of hypervelocity cratering is given by flash radiographs of craters during formation. In such x-ray pictures of the target silhouette, the ejection of sharp-edged particles from the target at various times after impact is apparent. The material ejected is clearly in the form of crystalline fragments and not liquid drops. A sequence of radiographs for a steel projectile colliding with an aluminum target[14] is shown in Figure 3.11, where the development of the crater up to 527×10^{-6} seconds after impact is shown.

Other experiments which demonstrate the crystallographic nature of cratering are those in which single crystals are used as targets. In these cases the craters formed are not of circular cross sections, but take on shapes corresponding to the crystal orientations and slip directions. For instance, Gehring and Richards[9] reported triangular-shaped craters for particles fired into a (111) face of a copper single crystal, square craters for a (100) face, and shield-shaped craters for

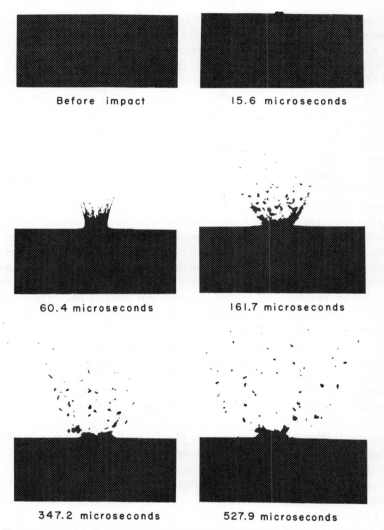

Before impact   15.6 microseconds

60.4 microseconds   161.7 microseconds

347.2 microseconds   527.9 microseconds

Fig. 3.11. Sequence of flash radiographs showing development of a crater in aluminum at various times after impact, as marked. Note particularly the sharp-edged large fragments of target material evident in the later radiographs, and the large final crater size relative to the projectile diameter. The results are for a 0.2-gram steel projectile fired into a semi-infinite 2S aluminum target block at a velocity of 3.5×10^5 cm/sec. (Photographs by courtesy of C. M. Glass, Ballistics Research Laboratories, Aberdeen Proving Ground, Maryland.)

a (112) face. This is in perfect agreement with the particle-wave view, since ejection of material from the target should occur preferentially from the slip directions (directions of closest spacing) where the momentum transfer constant is greatest. Anisotropic craters formed in aluminum single crystals and bicrystals have also been reported by Glass and Pond[15] who conclude that "the concept that the material being deformed acts as a fluid for the duration of the load can be shown to be incorrect." A similar conclusion was indicated by the work of Rinehart,[16] who detonated a charge within a hollow single crystal of aluminum. The axis of the hollow cylinder was in a ⟨102⟩ direction and the deformation produced exhibited a twofold symmetry that was unambiguously related to the orientation of stress with respect to the crystallographic axes and the slip systems. Similar conclusions were reached by Glass and Moss[17] from internal explosive loading of hollow copper and aluminum single crystals, and also from surface explosions on single-crystal samples. A square crater formed on the surface of a large aluminum single crystal from such an explosion is shown in Figure 3.12.

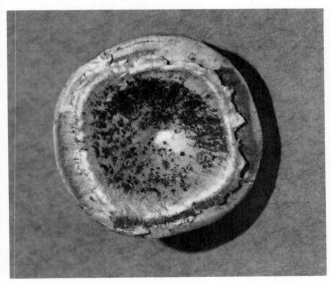

Fig. 3.12. Squared crater formed by an explosive charge detonated on the surface of a single crystal of aluminum. (Reference 17; specimen by courtesy of C. M. Glass and G. L. Moss, Ballistics Research Laboratories, Aberdeen Proving Ground, Maryland.)

All of these descriptions of the formation of craters in metals at hypervelocities, and the anisotropic nature of single-crystal high-speed deformations, offer strong qualitative support of the particle-wave approach to impact and deformation. We also note that from particle-wave theory a threshold velocity, v_f, is predicted, above which lattice breakup, and therefore cratering, begins. Hence, if data are available showing at what velocities cratering begins in various materials, an opportunity for a quantitative check exists. There are data giving crater depth as a function of velocity for various materials as shown, for example,[18] in Figures 3.13 and 3.14. Unfortunately, the velocity range studied in these two instances (aluminum spheres against aluminum targets, and copper spheres against copper targets) did not extend to sufficiently low velocities to sharply define the threshold values. However, we do see from these data that the predicted threshold values (indicated on the curves) for both aluminum and copper are definitely of the right order of magnitude. In using crater depth as a measure of the cratering process, we must be very careful to distinguish between a crater and an indentation.

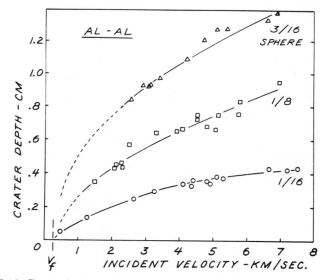

Fig. 3.13. Crater depth vs. incident velocity for various diameter aluminum spheres against semi-infinite aluminum targets. (Data from Olive G. Engel.[18]) Predicted threshhold velocity, v_f, from Table 3.1 is 0.29 km/sec, as marked.

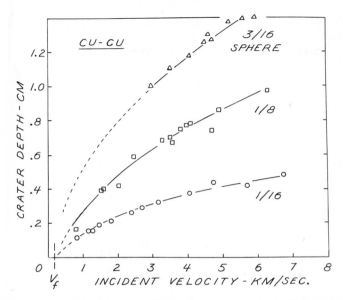

Fig. 3.14. Crater depth vs. incident velocity for various diameter copper spheres against semi-infinite copper targets. (Data from Olive G. Engel.[18]) Predicted threshold velocity, v_f, from Table 3.1 is 0.19 km/sec, as marked.

The latter can be formed by merely pressing the projectile against the target face in a very slow "static" test, particularly when the projectile is of a harder material than the target. Such an indentation would be produced by internal free particles in the target with velocities greater than v_1, whereas the cratering process cannot start until free-particle velocities reach v_f. Hence, for our purpose in checking the predicted values of v_f, data in which soft projectiles strike the same or a harder target material are needed. In addition, the velocity values given will be significant only if these are known relative to the target at impact; in real (as opposed to ideal) collisions, this is possible only if (1) the target is of exactly the same material, mass, and shape as the projectile, or (2) the target is of infinite mass and extent compared to the projectile. In the first case (1), the relevant impact velocity will be one-half the projectile velocity before impact, while in the second case (2), the impact velocity will be equal to the projectile velocity before impact. The values of v_f calculated are for free-particle velocities of individual atoms against a monatomic lattice;

in order to relate these to the macroscopic projectile velocity for collisions where the semi-infinite target and the projectile are of the same material, we note that all of the projectile atoms are free insofar as the target lattice is concerned. The same is true of surface target atoms with respect to lattice atoms within the projectile. Thus, not only will pieces of the target fly off against the incoming projectile, but pieces of the projectile will also fly off against the target, leading to the disintegration (and even complete disappearance) of the projectile. For dissimilar projectile–target materials, the projectile velocity for fission will be a function of the atomic-mass ratios of target–projectile atoms according to

$$v'_f = v_f m_t / m_p \qquad (3.30)$$

where v_f is the fission velocity of the target material, m_t is the mass of the target atom, m_p is the mass of the projectile atom, and v'_f is the projectile velocity for fission of a semi-infinite target.

Thus, according to Eq. 3.30, the projectile threshold velocity for copper pellets against aluminum targets will be lowered to 1.23×10^4 cm/sec, while aluminum pellets against copper targets will produce cratering above 4.5×10^4 cm/sec. Data for these cases are given by Engel,[18] but again are not sufficient to allow an exact check, although they are consistent with the above conclusions. We do note that, according to this idea, it should be possible to produce cratering in aluminum with copper projectiles *without* projectile fission in the velocity range between 1.23 and 4.5×10^4 cm/sec.

A good test of the predicted threshold velocity for cratering is provided by experiments in which liquid drops are impacted against solid targets (the targets are actually fired against the liquid drops in this case). It is not ordinarily possible to produce indentations in a metal by pressing liquid drops against the metal surface, so that, in this case, the measured pit depths can be taken as a more reliable indication of cratering only, rather than as a combination of "static" indentation and cratering. Pitting of metals caused by impact with liquid drops has been studied by Engel,[19] and the pits or craters formed are in every respect similar to those formed in metal impact. Unfortunately for our purposes, the targets used by Engel were not large enough to be considered semi-infinite from the standpoint of either relative thickness or mass in most cases, but the projectile threshold velocity,

v_f', for cratering in a semi-infinite target can be calculated and compared with some of the data listed by Engel. Because of the small size of the targets used, they can be considered to approach semi-infinity only for heavy metals, like lead and, perhaps, copper, when mercury drops are used. Pit-depth data for 0.1- and 0.285-cm mercury drops against lead targets are shown in Figure 3.15. The data agree fairly

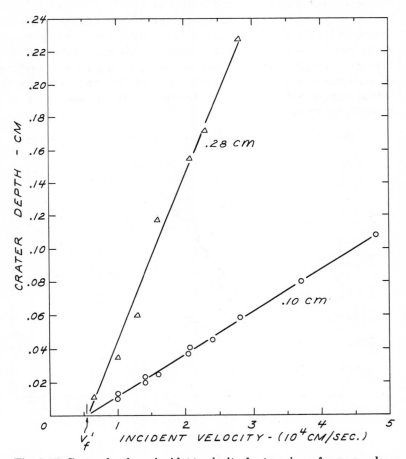

Fig. 3.15. Crater depth vs. incident velocity for two sizes of mercury drops impacting lead target plates. (Data from Olive G. Engel.[19]) The predicted threshold velocity, v_f', from Table 3.1 and Eq. 3.30, is 0.54×10^4 cm/sec, as marked.

well with the predicted value for v_f' of 0.54 × 10⁴ cm/sec. Similar data for 0.1- and 0.2-cm mercury drops against annealed electrolytic copper[19] are given in Figure 3.16, and again agree reasonably well with the predicted v_f' of 0.60 × 10⁴ cm/sec for this case. We notice that in both of these instances v_f' is independent of drop size as it should be. Above v_f', of course, the larger drops produce larger craters, but both sizes start producing craters at exactly the same velocity. Collisions of mercury drops against aluminum targets were also described by Engel,[19] but the targets clearly did not even approach an infinite mass relative to the drops in this case; values of drop velocity at which cratering commenced were higher than predicted on the basis of semi-infinite targets, as would be expected, since the actual impact velocity is some fraction of the projectile or drop velocity for small targets.

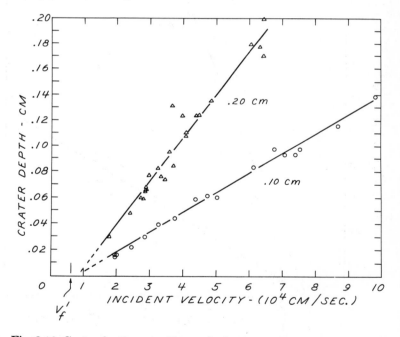

Fig. 3.16. Crater depth vs. incident velocity for two sizes of mercury drops impacting copper target plates. (Data from Olive G. Engel.[20]) The predicted threshold velocity, v_f' from Table 3.1 and Eq. 3.30, is 0.60 × 10⁴ cm/sec, as marked.

Finally, in Figures 3.17 and 3.18 are shown curves of crater depth vs. projectile velocity for solid spheres of iron and aluminum fired into semi-infinite targets of the same material.[19] Here, the predicted values of v_f apply directly and agree well with experimental values from these somewhat scattered data.

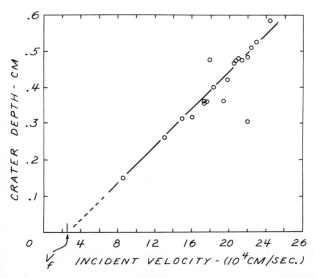

Fig. 3.17. Crater depth vs. projectile velocity for 0.483-cm iron spheres fired into semi-infinite iron targets. (Data from references 5 and 19). The predicted value of v_f from Table 3.1 is 2.36 × 10⁴ cm/sec, as marked.

Some of the consequences of reversed lattice motion at velocities below v_f are susceptible to experimental verification through impact studies of the type carried out by Bell.[20] Bell has developed a remarkable technique of measuring strain in free-flight impact tests through the use of diffraction gratings ruled directly on cylindrical test specimens. Target and hitter specimens are of identical material and dimensions (often 10-in. long and 1-in. diameter), so that the impact velocity is always one-half of the hitter velocity before impact. The impact occurs with both the hitter and target specimen "free." Strain measurements in the target specimen have been made to within 0.020 in. from the impact face, using diffraction gratings 0.001–0.005-ın. long with about 30,000 lines to the inch. This technique is obviously

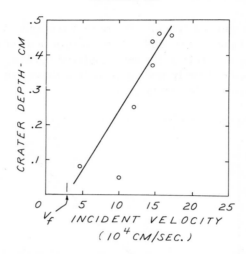

Fig. 3.18. Crater depth vs. projectile velocity for 0.483-cm aluminum spheres fired into semi-infinite aluminum targets. (Data from references 5 and 19). The predicted value of v_f from Table 3.1 is 2.92×10^4 cm/sec, as marked.

capable of detecting possible transitory effects or excited states of the type discussed previously.

One result of Bell's measurements is that a hydrodynamic transition velocity is observed[21] above which "excessive mushrooming in the first diameter is experimentally observed." The values for this transition velocity have been determined for both aluminum and copper; in the former case, the value is based on approximately 400 separate tests. From our previous discussion of reversed lattice motion, we identify the Bell transition velocity as $2v_1$ and make the following comparisons:

	Al	Cu
"Hydrodynamic" transition velocity measured by Bell	2050 in./sec (±50 in./sec)	980 in./sec (±20 in./sec)
$2v_1$	2039 in./sec (5710 cm/sec)	968 in./sec (2458 cm/sec)

The agreement can only be interpreted as a confirmation of our point of view that particle momentum waves play a dominant role in mechanical deformation.

Bell has also reported another critical velocity in aluminum[22] of 582 in./sec, *below* which he notes the following characteristics: "A large delay in the development of strain, *a lack of mushrooming*, a lack of reproducibility in the data in the immediate vicinity of the impact face." From our previous comments on the $|v_t|$ vs. v_1' curves and transient vs. equilibrium behavior in deformation, we expect just such unstable behavior and the onset of mushrooming to start somewhere between $0.5v_1$ and $0.75v_1$ or between 508 and 765 in./sec, depending on the exact slope of the momentum load line.

Additional evidence of a different kind can also be cited to substantiate the existence of the limiting velocities, v_f, in nonmetallic crystals. Although only monatomic crystals have been discussed so far, it is possible to apply some of the same ideas to diatomic cubic crystals like the alkali halides. In order to apply the monatomic development directly, the alkali halide crystals are considered to be two interpenetrating monatomic fcc lattices with masses, m_a and m_b, respectively. Then *pairs* of limiting velocities, v_{1a} and v_{1b}, can be calculated for each such diatomic crystal

$$v_{1a} = h/2m_a \boldsymbol{d}_1$$

$$v_{1b} = h/2m_b \boldsymbol{d}_1 \tag{3.31}$$

These pairs of limiting velocities, in turn, lead to a prediction of two final or fission free-particle velocities for each diatomic crystal.

$$v_{fa} \cong \sqrt{v_{1a} \cdot \boldsymbol{c}_s}$$

$$v_{fb} \cong \sqrt{v_{1b} \cdot \boldsymbol{c}_s} \tag{3.32}$$

where $\boldsymbol{c}_s$ is the mean sound velocity for the diatomic crystal, as previously defined by Eq. 3.25. This view of diatomic crystals is one in which particle momentum waves are pictured as travelling along monatomic rows such as —Na—Na—Na— and —Cl—Cl—Cl— in NaCl, for example. It is interesting to note that slip in these crystals does occur along such $\langle 1\bar{1}0 \rangle$ directions, which are those with closest atomic spacings ($\boldsymbol{d}_1$) for the interpenetrating *monatomic* fcc component lattices. The possibility of particle wave propagation in $\langle 100 \rangle$ directions in diatomic cubic crystals is not ruled out, but will be considered in detail elsewhere.

Johnston and Gilman[23] have measured the *average* velocities of individual dislocations in lithium fluoride (LiF) crystals under various loads, including short stress pulses of about 10^{-6} seconds duration produced by impact. Their results showed the existence of two separate curves of velocity vs. applied shear stress; these were attributed to screw and edge dislocations. However, from the particle-wave view, the existence of two velocity branches would also be predicted for a diatomic crystal like LiF, and two final or maximum dislocation velocities are therefore also predicted; these agree well with the maximum values of dislocation velocities actually found by

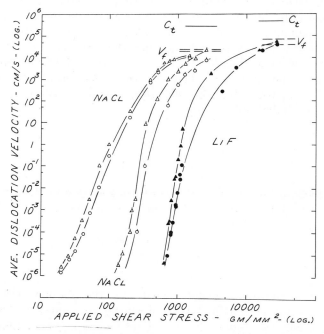

Fig. 3.19. Average dislocation velocity vs. applied shear stress for LiF and NaCl crystals, as reported by Johnston and Gilman[23] and Gutmanas et al.[24] The experimental values of velocity are seen to level off close to the predicted values of v_f, as marked, and not at the much higher sound velocities, c_t, as expected from elastic-dislocation theories. The values of v_f are calculated on the assumption that these diatomic crystals can be considered as two interpenetrating monatomic fcc crystals with different atomic masses, as discussed in the text.

Johnston and Gilman, as shown by the horizontal dashed lines in Figure 3.19 where their data are reproduced. Also shown in Figure 3.19 are curves of average dislocation velocity vs. applied stress for two samples of sodium chloride (NaCl) from the data of Gutmanas, Nadgornyi, and Stepanov,[24] which was obtained by a method similar to that of Johnston and Gilman. As in the case of LiF, the curves for NaCl appear to bend over, as if approaching maxima at the higher stresses. The predicted values again agree well with the limiting experimental values, as demonstrated by the dashed horizontal lines in Figure 3.19. In any case, it is very clear from the data that the maximum values of dislocation velocity predicted on the basis of the particle-wave approach to deformation are in much better agreement with the experimental results than the corresponding predictions from conventional dislocation theories based solely on elastic concepts. These latter theories predict that the limiting dislocation velocity equals the speed of sound, c_t, in the crystal; a predicted value, which in these cases, at least, is about ten times too high.

Conclusions

The particle-wave view of deformation in solids leads to expectations of strange behavior at high velocities; the experimental observations of high-velocity impact bear out these peculiar predictions and thus lend strong qualitative support to the ideas advanced. In particular, the phenomenon of hypervelocity cratering fits in well with the concept of reverse lattice motion required to allow particle-wave propagation at high velocities (above v_1). The crystallographic nature of the observed cratering process also supports the particle-wave approach.

Some of the results of lower-velocity impact tests, such as the occurrence of instabilities and transition velocities, are also in accord with particle-wave ideas.

In addition, it is possible to calculate certain characteristic velocities, v_1, $2v_1$, v_f, and v_f' in terms of fundamental constants and measured values of lattice dissociation energy or elastic sound velocities. A total of 440 such velocities have been calculated for 20 monatomic cubic metals; in only ten cases are experimental data available for comparison; the agreement is good or excellent in all ten instances, however.

By introducing the concept of phonon fission and an associated conversion of "phonon mass" to energy, it is possible to suggest a relationship between lattice dissociation energy per atom and a mean sound velocity, c_s, in a crystal, viz.

$$D = mc_s^2$$

where c_s depends on the translational and longitudinal sound velocities. This relation is, in fact, verified for 18 of the 20 cubic metals tried; sound velocity data were not available in two cases.

The success of the particle-wave view in dealing with hypervelocity impact and the previous success in explaining the occurrence of non-elastic audio-frequency modes lend considerable support to the ideas advanced in the first chapter of this book. However, any satisfactory description of deformation must also provide a stress–strain law in agreement with experiment. Hence, a general stress–strain law derived from particle-wave concepts will be presented in the next chapter.

References

1. A. H. Cottrell, *The Mechanical Properties of Matter*, Wiley, New York, 1964.
2. K. R. Spangenberg, *Fundamentals of Electron Devices*, McGraw-Hill, New York, 1957, pp. 188, 362, and 363.
3. E. R. Fitzgerald, *Particle Waves and Mechanical Properties of Solids*, to be published.
4. E. R. Fitzgerald, *Phys. Letters*, **10**, 42–43 (1964).
5. W. S. Partridge, H. B. Vanfleet, and C. R. Whited, *J. Appl. Phys.*, **29**, 1332–1336 (1958).
6. M. E. Van Valkenburg, W. G. Clay, and J. H. Huth, *J. Appl. Phys.*, **27**, 1123–1129 (1956).
7. R. B. Pond, private communication.
8. J. P. Friichtenicht and B. Hameresh, *Proc. Fourth Symp. Hypervelocity Impact*, **3**, 39 (1960).
9. J. W. Gehring, Jr., and L. G. Richards, *Proc. Fourth Symp. Hypervelocity Impact*, **3**, 34 (1960).
10. E. N. Clark, A. Mackenzie, F. H. Schmitt, and I. L. Kintish, *Proc. Fourth Symp. Hypervelocity Impact*, **1**, 9 (1960).
11. J. H. Kineke, Jr., *Proc. Fourth Symp. Hypervelocity Impact*, **1**, 10 (1960).
12. A. M. Worthington, *Proc. Roy. Soc. London*, **34**, 217–230 (1882); *Phil. Trans. Roy. Soc. London*, **A189**, 137–148 (1897); *A Study of Splashes*, Longs, Green and Co., New York, 1908.
13. Olive G. Engel, *Collisions of Liquid Drops with Liquids*, Part II, Tech. Rept. No. WADD-TR-60-475, ASTIA, Arlington, Virginia.

14. C. M. Glass, private communication.
15. C. M. Glass and R. B. Pond, *Proc. Fourth Symp. Hypervelocity Impact*, **3**, 35 (1960).
16. J. S. Rinehart, *J. Appl. Phys.*, **26**, 1315–1317 (1955).
17. C. M. Glass, G. L. Moss, and S. K. Golaski, in *Response of Metals to High Velocity Deformation*, P. G. Shewmon and V. F. Zackay, Eds., Interscience, New York, 1961, pp. 115–141.
18. Olive G. Engel, *Proc. Sixth Symp. Hypervelocity Impact*, **2**, 337–366 (1963).
19. Olive G. Engel, *J. Res. Natl. Bur. Std.*, **62**, 229–246 (1959); **64A**, 61–72 (1960).
20. J. F. Bell, *J. Appl. Phys.*, **27**, 1109–1113 (1956); **31**, 277–282 (1959).
21. J. F. Bell and J. H. Suckling, *Proc. Fourth U. S. Natl. Congr. Appl. Mech.*, 877–883 (1963); J. F. Bell, in *Stress Waves in Anelastic Solids*, H. Kolsky and W. Prager, Eds., Springer-Verlag, Berlin, 1964, pp. 167–182.
22. J. F. Bell, *J. Appl. Phys.*, **31**, 2188–2195 (1960); **32**, 1982–1993 (1961).
23. W. G. Johnston and J. J. Gilman, *J. Appl. Phys.*, **30**, 129–144 (1959).
24. E. Y. Gutmanas, E. M. Nadgornyi, and A. V. Stepanov, *Soviet Phys.-Solid State*, **5**, 743–747 (1963).

IV

STRESS–STRAIN LAW FOR CRYSTALLINE SOLIDS

Introduction

In introducing the idea of internal generation of particle waves in crystals in the first chapter of this book, brief mention was made of the necessity for a connection between external mechanical load and the generated waves. It was suggested that field-free particles in a crystal are accelerated by mechanical loading of the crystal. As a result of this acceleration, after some very short generation time, t_g, the field-free atoms acquire a velocity, v, and corresponding wavelengths, $\lambda = h/mv$. The waves associated with such field-free particles then propagate through the periodic potential field of the crystal lattice as particle *momentum waves* and produce the effects attributed to plastic deformation or slip. Through a careful choice of experiments, we have so far been able to substantiate the ideas advanced by measurements of *frequencies* and *velocities* in place of the usual mechanical variables of load and deformation (or stress and strain). Some large deformation effects, such as flaring out and necking down, the formation of craters, and the ejection of crystal fragments in hypervelocity impact have also been described by the particle wave approach. Next we turn to a consideration of the exact form of the relation between internal incident velocity of field-free particles and mechanical load. From such a relation, we hope to be able to construct a stress–strain curve for real materials which will compare favorably with experimental observations.

1. Stress Dependence of Free-Particle Velocity

Consider a particular atom in a monatomic lattice to be in a field-free region extending along a fractional distance, pd_1, in a direction of lattice spacing, d_1, as shown in Figure 4.1. This local field-free region represents a perturbation of the periodic potential of the perfect crystal lattice resulting from dislocations or other defects, as described previously. In any case, this atom is considered to be "free" in the

102

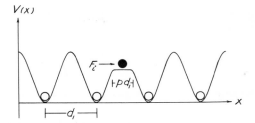

Fig. 4.1. Schematic diagram showing field-free interlattice atom (filled circle) in a lattice of spacing d_1 and periodic potential, $V(x)$, as indicated. Field-free distance is pd_1, where $p < 1$.

indicated direction over a very limited distance, pd_1, where $p \ll 1$. The question now is: What internal force, F_i, must be applied to the atom to have it reach a certain velocity, v_i, before it passes out of the field-free region? Having attained this velocity just "outside" the periodic field of the crystal (but from an "inside" position!), the atom is expected to propagate through the periodic structure ahead as a particle momentum wave. As shown previously, the connection between force and velocity is easily obtained by setting the work done by the force, F_i, through the distance, pd_1, equal to the final kinetic energy of the free particle.

$$F_i \, pd_1 = \frac{1}{2}mv_i^2$$

or

$$F_i = \frac{1}{2p} \frac{m}{d_1} v_i^2 \tag{4.1}$$

The generating time, t_g, needed by the free particle to reach the velocity, v_i, is also easily found

$$t_g = v_i/a = mv_i/F_i \tag{4.2}$$

where the acceleration, a, is given by F_i/m. By substitution for v_i from Eq. 4.1, this time can be given in terms of F_i and the lattice constants

$$t_g = \sqrt{2p\,d_1m/F_i} \tag{4.3}$$

If Y_i is the average force per unit area (stress) in the direction of d_1, then a stress–velocity relation can be written,

$$Y_i \text{ (force/area)} = F_i \zeta = \frac{1}{2p} \frac{\zeta m}{d_1} v_i^2 \qquad (4.4)$$

where ζ is the number of atoms per unit area in the relevant cross section.

The stress–velocity relation of Eq. 4.4 can be written in terms of a density, ρ, for a given crystal structure since it is always possible to write a density relation of the type

$$\frac{\zeta m}{d_1} = \gamma \rho \qquad (4.5)$$

where γ is a purely numerical factor; γ is $\sqrt{2/3}$ for a (111) plane of a fcc crystal, for example. In terms of density, Eq. 4.4 becomes

$$Y_i = \frac{\gamma}{2p} \rho v_i^2 \qquad (4.6)$$

So far, internal forces or stresses in the field-free direction, pd_1, have been assumed, but a relation between an external stress of arbitrary orientation relative to d_1 can also be written in terms of a stress-orientation factor, Ω, such that[1]

$$\Omega = \cos \alpha \cos \beta \qquad (4.7)$$

where

$$Y_i = Y_0 \cos \alpha \cos \beta \qquad (4.8)$$

as shown in Figure 4.2. Here, F/A is the external stress, Y_0; α is the angle between the normal to the active slip plane and the external load; and β is the angle between the slip direction in the plane and the load. The relation between an arbitrary external stress and internal field-free particle velocity thus becomes

$$Y_0 = \frac{\gamma}{\Omega} \frac{1}{2p} \rho v_i^2 \qquad (4.9)$$

The orientation factor, Ω, is always unambiguously defined for a single crystal and a particular slip direction, but a mean value, $\bar{\Omega}$, must be calculated for polycrystalline samples, as discussed by Sachs,[2] Taylor,[3] and Bishop and Hill.[4]

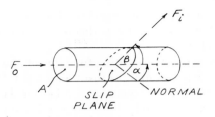

Fig. 4.2. Diagram used to obtain the relation between the force, F_i, in the slip direction on a slip plane and an external force, F_0, acting on a cylindrical crystal sample $(F_i = F_0 \cos \beta)$. The relation between external stress, Y_0, and stress Y_i in the slip direction on the slip plane also follows $(Y_i = Y_0 \cos \alpha \cos \beta)$ from the diagram.

In a particular crystal, all field-free atoms cannot be expected to be in exactly the same field-free region, pd; rather, some kind of distribution of pd will exist, leading to a distribution of the velocities, v_i, for a given uniform external stress. In order to take this distribution into account, a mean value, $\bar{p}$, can be assumed, corresponding to a mean internal velocity, $\bar{v}_i$, for the field-free particles in a crystal. The mean field-free distance parameter will depend on the exact defect structure of a particular sample and give a good approximation to the actual stress–velocity relation only if some type of "normal" distribution of field-free distances exists. Among other factors, $\bar{p}$ may depend on impurity content, previous work hardening undergone by the sample, thermal history, and, in polycrystals, grain size.

From Eq. 4.9 and a mean value of p, it is possible, however, to relate the characteristic velocities mentioned in the third chapter to certain characteristic external stresses:

$$Y_{01} = \frac{\gamma}{\bar{\Omega}} \frac{1}{2\bar{p}} \rho v_1^2 \qquad (4.10)$$

$$Y_{0t} = \frac{\gamma}{\bar{\Omega}} \frac{1}{2\bar{p}} \rho (2v_1)^2 \qquad (4.11)$$

$$Y_{0f} = \frac{\gamma}{\bar{\Omega}} \frac{1}{2\bar{p}} \rho (v_f)^2 \qquad (4.12)$$

$$= \frac{\gamma}{\bar{\Omega}} \frac{1}{2\bar{p}} \rho v_1 c_s \qquad (4.12')$$

where γ, $\bar{\Omega}$, and $\bar{p}$ have the meanings just discussed; ρ is the density, $v_1 = h/2md_1$, $v_f \cong \sqrt{v_1 \cdot c_s}$, and c_s is the mean sound velocity defined in the preceding chapter.

The value of $\bar{p}$ will be a sensitive function of the detailed defect structure of a particular sample, as just pointed out. Therefore, while all the other factors in these equations can be calculated from fundamental material constants and a knowledge of the sample orientation relative to applied stress, it is impossible to predict an exact value of $\bar{p}$, and hence stress, in a particular case. The *internal incident* free-particle velocities at which characteristic macroscopic phenomena start are the same for all samples of a given material, but the *external stresses* needed to produce these velocities depend on the particular defect state of each sample. Only if $\bar{p}$ is the same will two samples of the same material show identical behavior under load.

This inability to predict the characteristic stress values for a material from its fundamental constants is, at first, rather disappointing. Experimental evidence, however, indicates that characteristic stress values for individual samples of the same material do often vary considerably. Thus, if the particle-wave view had provided for exact stress calculations, it would be in direct contradiction to experiment.

In addition to the difficulty in predicting an initial value of $\bar{p}$, it is evident that at velocities above v_1 where reversed lattice motion sets in (or above the instability point, between $0.5v_1$ and $0.75v_1$), distortion of the lattice will become increasingly severe and $\bar{p}$ may then change drastically as deformation proceeds. The mean orientation, $\bar{\Omega}$, can also change as a result of lattice motion, so that we do not expect these stress–velocity equations to be generally useful above stress levels corresponding to internal velocities greater than $v_1 = h/2md_1$.

In connection with these stress–velocity relations, it is interesting to note that Bell,[5] from impact tests, has experimentally demonstrated a connection between a transition velocity, v_t, and the elastic limit stress for fine-grained, fully annealed, commercially pure aluminum and copper, viz.

$$Y_{0e} \text{ (elastic limit)} = \rho v_t^2 \qquad \text{(Bell's elastic limit law)} \qquad (4.13)$$

A relation between observed peak stress and the product $v_t \cdot c_b$, where c_b is the elastic bar velocity ($c_b = \sqrt{E/\rho}$; E is Young's modulus) has also been reported by Bell,[7] where

$$Y_{0p} \text{ (peak)} = \rho v_t \cdot c_b \qquad \text{(Bell's peak stress law)} \qquad (4.14)$$

Bell's transition velocity, v_t, has already been identified[6] as $2v_1$, and the bar velocity will be proportional to the longitudinal sound velocity, c_ℓ, according to

$$c_b = jc_\ell \qquad (4.15)$$

where $j = 1$ for an infinitely thin bar; i.e., when the bar radius, r, is such that $r/\lambda \to 0$. Since v_f represents the highest internal field-free particle velocity which the lattice will support without disintegration, we can identify Y_{0f} with peak stress or at least write $Y_{0p} = fY_{0f}$, where f is a constant; similarily, an elastic limit stress, Y_{0e}, will be some fraction, f', of the reverse-flow stress, Y_{01}, and thus, from Eq. 4.10, we expect that

$$Y_{0e} = f' \frac{\gamma}{\bar{\Omega}} \frac{1}{2\bar{p}} \rho v_1^2 \qquad (4.16)$$

which compares with Bell's empirical finding for particular types of aluminum and copper,

$$Y_{0e} = 4\rho v_1^2 \qquad \text{(Bell)} \qquad (4.13')$$

if the quantity $\gamma f'/2\bar{\Omega}\bar{p}$ happens to equal 4 for the particular materials tested.

   In the same way, the peak stress from Eq. 4.12' becomes

$$Y_{0p} = f \frac{\gamma}{\bar{\Omega}} \frac{1}{2\bar{p}} \rho v_1 \cdot c_s \qquad (4.17)$$

which is similar to Bell's finding

$$Y_{0p} = \rho 2 v_1 \cdot j c_\ell \qquad \text{(Bell)} \qquad (4.14')$$

since the mean sound velocity, c_s, can always be related to the longitudinal sound velocity, c_ℓ. For example, in aluminum, $c_\ell = 1.98 c_s$

and in copper $c_\ell = 1.78c_s$. Thus, the predicted stress *ratios* from Eqs. 4.16 and 4.17 are

$$Y_{0p}/Y_{0e} = \frac{f \cdot c_s}{f' \cdot v_1}$$

$$= (f/f') \cdot \frac{c_\ell}{1.98v_1} \qquad \text{(aluminum)}$$

$$= (f/f') \cdot \frac{c_\ell}{1.78v_1} \qquad \text{(copper)}$$

which, for $f = f'$, are similar to Bell's experimental results

$$Y_{0p}/Y_{0e} \quad \text{(Bell)} = \frac{jc_\ell}{2v_1}$$

if the factor j is nearly 1.

2. Load–Displacement Curve for an Infinite Lattice

From the force–velocity relation just developed (Eq. 4.1) and the frequency–wave vector dependence previously found for particle waves in a lattice, it is possible to infer a force–displacement law for particle-wave propagation. In order to do this it is convenient to first recall, and then extend, some familiar elastic deformation concepts. An elastic interaction or force constant, K_e, can be defined in terms of the relative displacement, x_e, between atoms in a lattice in a static (slow) test

$$K_e = F/x_e \qquad (4.18)$$

In an ideal case, K_e may be constant for a range of values in x_e, but K_e can still be defined at each point of a nonlinear F–x_e curve by Eq. 4.18. Further, as long as K_e is understood to represent the F/x_e ratio at each point of a curve, then an F–x_e curve can be constructed from a corresponding K_e vs. F curve.

It is also possible to define K_e for elastic waves in terms of a dynamic experiment in which the phase velocity is measured. For an elastic wave in a one-dimensional lattice, it is easily shown that

$$K_e = \frac{m}{d^2} c_s^2 \qquad (4.19)$$

where $d/\lambda \to 0$ (continuous medium). For wavelengths *not* large compared to the lattice spacing, Eq. 4.19 can be used to define a variable, K_e, if the variation of c_s with λ (or wave vector, k) is known.

Turning now to particle waves, we can also measure the displacement, x_p, of a particular field-free atom, where x_p is measured from the original lattice position, as shown in Figure 4.3. A force constant, K'_ℓ, can also be defined for this case as

$$K'_\ell = F/x_p \tag{4.20}$$

but there are important differences between elastic and particle-wave displacements, as shown in Figure 4.3. The elastic displacements, x_e, represent increases in relative distances between atoms and are the same for all atoms under uniform load. In particle-wave deformation, not every atom is displaced; instead, only a fraction of the total atoms in a row move. If a particular lattice segment is chosen for observation, its length will not be changed until a field-free atom has

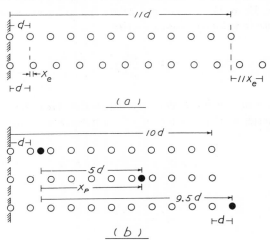

Fig. 4.3. (*a*) Increase in length of a 12-atom lattice segment resulting from an elastic displacement, x_e, of each atom from its nearest neighbor. (*b*) Increase in length of a 12-atom lattice segment resulting from a particle-wave displacement, x_p, of a field-free atom (filled circle) initially at the second interlattice position (top) from the left as it moves through the lattice as a particle wave (center) and finally emerges at the right (bottom).

moved to the end of the segment. The change in length of the 12-atom segment shown in Figure 4.3 increases from $11d$ to $11(d + x_e)$ for very small elastic displacements, x_e, but a similar segment changes length from $10d$ to $11d$ only for a particle-wave displacement, x_p, of $10d$. Of course, fractional deformations can be defined for a particular segment length, S,

$$\Delta s_p = \frac{x_p}{S}\, d \qquad (4.21)$$

and such smoothed-out, fractional displacements will be discussed in more detail later.

A dynamic force constant, K'_ℓ, can also be defined for particle waves in a lattice in terms of a phase velocity, c_p,

$$K'_\ell = \frac{m}{d^2}\, c_p^2 \qquad (4.22)$$

An expression for c_p as a function of wave vector, k, was found in the first chapter. From the de Broglie relationship between wave vector and free particle velocity, we can write

$$v^2 = \frac{\hbar^2}{m^2}\, k^2 \qquad (4.23)$$

and by means of the force–velocity expression (Eq. 4.1) derived for field-free particles in a lattice, a relation between force and wave vector results

$$F = \alpha^2 k^2 \qquad k = \sqrt{F/\alpha} \qquad (4.24)$$

where

$$\alpha^2 = \frac{\hbar^2}{2p\,dm}$$

Hence the expression for K'_ℓ becomes (upon substitution of c_p from Eq. 1.33 into Eq. 4.22)

$$K'_\ell = \frac{\hbar^2}{4md^2}\, k^2 \cdot \left[\sin^2\left(\frac{kd}{2}\right) \middle/ \left(\frac{kd}{2}\right)^2 \right]^2 \qquad (4.25)$$

Substitutions for k and K'_t, made from Eqs. 4.24 and 4.20, lead to a displacement–force law for particle waves

$$x = \frac{2d}{p}\left[\frac{b\sqrt{F}}{\sin b\sqrt{F}}\right]^4 \tag{4.26}$$

where

$$b = d/2\alpha = \frac{d}{\hbar}\sqrt{\frac{p\,dm}{2}}$$

Since all of these remarks so far have been in terms of a stationary lattice, Eq. 4.26 can only be expected to apply to values of F such that the generated free-particle velocity is less than $v_1 = h/2md$. The limit on force in Eq. 4.26 is thus

$$F_1 = \frac{h^2}{8pm\,d^3} \tag{4.27}$$

where $b\sqrt{F_1} = \pi/2$, $\sin b\sqrt{F} = 1$, and the corresponding displacement is

$$x_1 = \frac{2d}{p}\left(\frac{\pi}{2}\right)^4 \tag{4.28}$$

A graph of this force–displacement law is shown in Figure 4.4. The displacement has an initial value, $x_0 = 2d/p$, at zero force, and the curve then rises with decreasing slope to the terminal point at F_1, x_1, where reverse lattice motion sets in; beyond this point, local reverse motion of the lattice results in decreasing values of effective lattice spacing, d', such that the wavelength, λ', associated with any incident particle-wave velocity, v', above v_1 is just equal to $2d'$. Then, if displacement and velocity are measured relative to a fixed reference point *external* to the lattice, the propagation (phase) velocity will be constant for forces above F_1 and equal to the value at F_1.

$$c_1 = \frac{v_1}{2}\left(\frac{2}{\pi}\right)^2 = \frac{2v_1}{\pi^2} = \frac{h}{m\,d\pi^2} \tag{4.29}$$

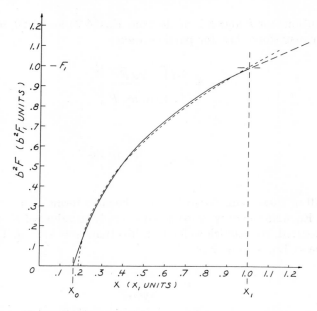

Fig. 4.4. Force–displacement law (solid line) for a particle wave in an infinite lattice of spacing d, according to Eq. 4.26 of the text. The factor b depends on the field-free parameter, p, (Fig. 4.1.), Planck's constant, the atomic mass, and the lattice spacing. F_1 is the force above which reverse lattice motion must occur. The dashed line shows a parabolic F–x law for comparison.

Thus, from Eq. 4.22

$$K'_t = \frac{m}{d^2}\, \frac{4v_1^2}{\pi^4} \tag{4.30}$$

or

$$F = \frac{m}{d^2}\, \frac{4v_1^2}{\pi^4}\, x \tag{4.31}$$

for $F > F_1$ and $x > x_1$.

Eq. 4.31 can be rewritten for comparison with Eq. 4.26 for velocities below v_1

$$x = \frac{m d^4 \pi^4}{h^2}\, F \tag{4.32}$$

This equation not only predicts a linear relation between F and x above the limiting fixed-lattice stress, F_1, but also indicates that the relation is independent of the defect-structure parameter, $\bar{p}$, at high loads.

Although really independent of $\bar{p}$, the displacement–force law of Eq. 4.32 can be written in terms of $\bar{p}$ and the constant b for purposes of comparison with the low-force law of Eq. 4.26.

$$x = \left(\frac{\pi}{2} \right)^2 \frac{2d}{p} b^2 F \qquad (4.33)$$

A plot of b^2F vs. x is shown in Figure 4.5 for both the low- and high-force laws (Eqs. 4.26 and 4.33); the two curves fit together smoothly (same slope) at F_1, x_1.

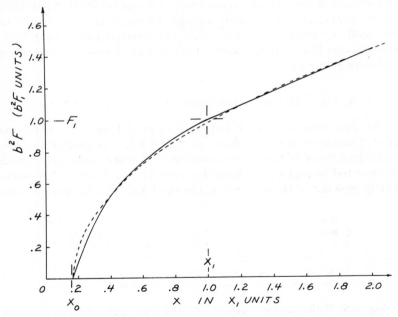

Fig. 4.5. Force–displacement law (solid line) for a particle wave in an infinite lattice of spacing, d, below and above the critical force, F_1. Above F_1, the relation is linear, as given by Eqs. 4.32 and 4.33 of the text, while below F_1, the relation is the same as that shown in Figure 4.4. A parabolic F–x curve (dashed line) is again shown for comparison.

As emphasized previously, the displacement, x, (or x_p) in this curve is only that of a particular field-free atom measured relative to an external fixed origin, and does not represent the elongation or strain of the lattice. We do expect, however, that the deformation of a crystal sample will depend in some fashion on the particle-wave displacement in the lattice. A relationship between displacement and deformation in a finite lattice will be brought forth in the next section.

Before considering finite lattices, it is interesting to note that these force-displacement laws can be very closely approximated by a parabolic law of the form

$$b^2 F = \beta (x - x_0)^{1/2} \qquad (4.34)$$

as indicated by the dashed lines in Figures 4.4 and 4.5. This fact is of importance because many experimental data can be fitted to parabolic stress–strain laws, particularly at high deformations.[8,9] Actually, as we shall see later, the stress–strain law derived from these load–deformation laws may be exactly parabolic at stresses corresponding to forces above F_1.

3. Load–Deformation Curve for a Finite Lattice

We next consider a finite lattice segment of length, S, containing $N + 1$ masses (atoms), as shown in Figure 4.6. The interlattice mass near the left end of the segment represents a field-free particle, which is expected to propagate along the segment as a wave and to eventually pass out of the segment at the right end. The frequency–wave

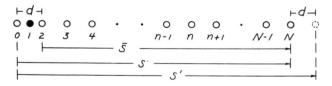

Fig. 4.6. Finite lattice segment, S, with interlattice field-free particle (solid circle) at left end. As a result of force applied, the field-free particle propagates through the partial lattice segment, $\bar{S}$, and finally reaches a terminal position at the right end of the segment (dashed circle), at which time the length of the $(N + 1)$ lattice segment changes from $S = (N - 1)d$ to $S' = Nd$.

vector relation for a finite lattice is exactly the same form as that for an infinite lattice, as emphasized in the second article. Hence, all of the preceding development applies, and the same x–F relation is obtained, but now only certain discrete values of F are allowed below F_1, as indicated in Eq. 4.35.

$$F_{pq} = \alpha^2 \left(\frac{\pi}{N d}\right)^2 \cdot q^2 \qquad (4.35)$$

$$= \frac{h^2}{8 \bar{p} m d} \frac{q^2}{\bar{S}^2} \qquad (4.35')$$

where $\bar{S} = (N - 2)d \cong N d = S$ for large N

$$q = 1, 2, 3 \ldots (N - 3)$$

There is a minimum force, F_{p1}, below which no displacement occurs, given by

$$F_{p1} = \frac{h^2}{8 \bar{p} m d S^2} \qquad \text{(lower limit)} \qquad (4.36)$$

as well as the upper limit (Eq. 4.27) for a stationary lattice

$$F_1 = \frac{h^2}{8 \bar{p} m d^3} \qquad \text{(upper limit)} \qquad (4.37)$$

where $F_{p1} = F_1/N^2$. Thus, the force–displacement curve for a finite lattice segment does not start at $F = 0$, but at some critical value, $F_{p1} > 0$, which depends strongly on the inverse segment length, $1/S$, and the field-free parameter, $\bar{p}$. Further, only certain discrete values of F result in displacement; the spacing between allowed force values increases with F, provided both S and p remain constant. Above F_1, however, reverse lattice motion sets in and the same smooth high-force law previously derived holds, as shown in Figure 4.7.

Returning now to the finite lattice segment of Figure 4.6, we notice that the length of the segment will suddenly change by an amount, d, when the particle-wave displacement equals S. As indicated earlier,

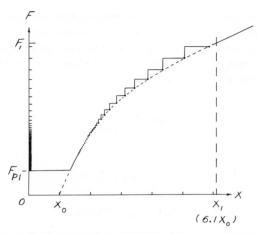

Fig. 4.7. Force–displacement law (solid line) for a particle wave propagating in a finite lattice segment of length $S = Nd$, where d is the lattice spacing. Propagation of the particle wave (and hence, displacement) results only for certain discrete values of force, F_{pq}, as given in Eq. 4.35 of the text. No particle-wave propagation occurs below a minimum value of force, F_{p1}, which varies inversely with the square of the segment length. The envelope of the F–x curve shown by the dashed line is the same as that for an infinite lattice (Fig. 4.4); note that above F_1 a continuous, linear relation between F and x prevails.

a smoothed or fractional change in length (anticipatory deformation) can be defined for values of x less than S by

$$\Delta s_p = \frac{x}{S} \cdot d \qquad (4.38)$$

$$\cong \frac{x}{N} \qquad (4.38')$$

To find Δs_p as a function of load, F, the appropriate displacement–force law is used to give x in Eq. 4.38. The elastic deformation produced in the lattice can also be calculated for a uniform force applied along the segment, producing an extension, $x_e = F/K_e$, between each atom pair, so that

$$\Delta s_e = N x_e = \frac{NF}{K_e} \qquad (4.39)$$

The total deformation (change in length) of the segment then becomes

$$\Delta s = \Delta s_e + \Delta s_{pq}$$

$$\Delta s = \frac{NF}{K_e} + \frac{x_0}{N} \left[\frac{b\sqrt{F_{pq}}}{\sin b\sqrt{F_{pq}}} \right]^4 \qquad (4.40)$$

where no particle-wave deformation occurs below F_{p1}; between F_{p1} and F_1, only discrete values of force produce particle-wave deformation; above F_1, smooth values of deformation again occur, according to

$$\Delta s = \frac{NF}{K_e} + \frac{1}{N} \cdot \frac{m d^4 \pi^4}{h^2} \cdot F \qquad (4.41)$$

The combined load–deformation curve for a single lattice segment is shown in Figure 4.8. This curve consists of (a) an initial, entirely elastic part for values of F below F_{p1}; (b) a part between F_{p1} and F_1

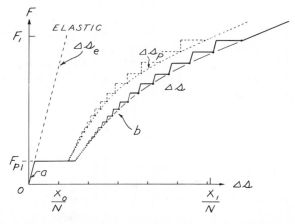

Fig. 4.8. Combined force–deformation curve (solid line) for elastic and particle-wave displacement in a finite lattice segment of spacing d and length $S = Nd$, where a smoothed, fractional deformation for particle-wave displacement is defined as $\Delta s_p = x d/S$. Separate elastic- and particle-wave contributions are indicated by the dashed lines, as marked. Below F_{p1}, (a) the deformation is elastic only; above, (b) both types of deformation occur.

where both elastic and discrete particle-wave deformations are present (the steps between allowed values of F_{pq} are no longer vertical, but have a slope N/K_e); and (c) a part above F_1 where both elastic and smooth particle-wave deformations occur. The critical force, F_{p1}, for the onset of plastic deformation decreases as N increases; the width of the particle-wave plateau also decreases with increasing N (and S), as does the deformation itself. On the other hand, the extent of elastic deformation at a given force increases with N. Hence, the combined curve may have no plateau or a plateau at zero force ($F_{p1} = 0$). The exact shapes of the curves depend on p and K_e, as well as N.

4. Frequency Dependence on Load

In connection with Eq. 4.35′ of the preceding section, it is interesting to recall the second chapter of this book, in which characteristic deformation frequencies were discussed. These were supposed to be given at low frequencies (for standing waves) by an expression

$$\nu_{pq} \cong \frac{h}{8mS^2} q^2 \tag{4.42}$$

and comparable frequencies were often observed for many materials, including aluminum and lead, where the atomic masses are quite different. Now, from Eq. 4.35′, we see that a given mode (e.g., $q = 1$) will indeed be identical for different metals, provided only that the product $F \cdot pd$ is the same, since

$$\frac{F \cdot pd}{h} = \frac{h}{8mS^2} = \nu_{p1} \tag{4.43}$$

Thus, by loading samples so that the product of pd and the force/atom in the slip direction are comparable, common frequencies of particle-wave modes are obtained. It is also clear that, in an evenly loaded sample, only a narrow band of lattice segments will be active and, hence, a sharp response to vibration of a particular frequency results, even though a wide distribution of segment lengths is present in the sample. Equation 4.43 can evidently be put into the form $F \cdot pd = h\nu_{pq}$, which shows the usual quantum relation between the work done on the field-free particle and the resulting particle-wave frequency in the lattice.

An exact expression relating frequency, ν_p, and the load per atom, F, can also be written by substituting for k in terms of F in the general frequency-wave vector relation previously derived for particle waves

$$\nu_{pq} = \nu_1 \sin^2 (b\sqrt{F_{pq}}) \qquad (4.44)$$

where $\nu_1 = \hbar/\pi m d^2$, and b and F_{pq} have their previous meanings, as defined in connection with Eqs. 4.26 and 4.35. The variation of frequency with force will then be as shown in Figure 4.9; in particular, at low (audio) frequencies, the dependence is linear. F can always be related to external stress through the proper orientation factor and a knowledge of the number of atoms per cross-sectional area, so that the frequency–stress variation should be of the same form as that given in Figure 4.9.

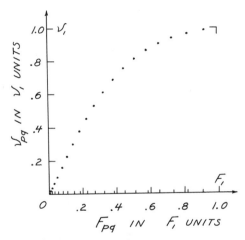

Fig. 4.9. Variation of particle-wave mode frequency, ν_{pq}, with force per atom, F_{pq}, for a finite lattice segment of spacing, d, and length, $S = Nd$. The case shown is for $N = 21$, with 20 discrete frequencies (modes) between ν_{p1} and ν_1. The envelope of the ν–F curve is sinusoidal, so that the initial portion is linear.

5. Stress–Strain Law for Three-Dimensional Crystals

Before extending the results to three-dimensions, it is instructive to consider a one-dimensional segment with several field-free (inter-lattice) masses, as in Figure 4.10. There may be Q such masses near one end of the segment, leading to an expression for the fractional deformation

$$\Delta s_p = Q \frac{x}{S} \, d_1 \qquad (4.45)$$

In the event that the field-free atoms are distributed through the segment as shown in the lower part of Figure 4.10, the *effective number* of equivalent full-length field-free atoms is increased. In the situation depicted, for example, the three masses must travel distances of S, $S/2$, and $S/4$ to contribute an extension, d_1, to the segment. The total fractional deformation for a displacement, x, of each field-free atom is then

$$\Delta s_p = \sum_{1}^{3} \Delta s_{pi} = \frac{x d_1}{S} + \frac{x d_1}{S/2} + \frac{x d_1}{S/4} = \frac{7 x d_1}{S} \qquad (4.46)$$

so that $Q' = 7$ (i.e., $Q' = 7Q/3$).

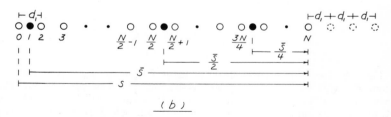

Fig. 4.10. (*a*) Finite lattice segment, S, with three field-free particles (filled circles) near the left end. The extension, Δs_p, as a function of the displacement, x, of each particle is $\Delta s_p = x d_1/\overline{S} + x d_1/\overline{S}' + x d_1/\overline{S}''$ or $\Delta s_p \cong 3\, x d_1/S$ for large N, where $S \cong \overline{S} = \overline{S}' = \overline{S}''$. (*b*) Finite lattice segment, S, with three field-free particles (filled circles) at various distances from the ends, as shown. $S = \overline{S}$ for large N and the extension, Δs_p, as a function of the displacement, x, is $\Delta s_p = 7\, x d_1/S$.

Let $f_i S$ = distance from field-free atom to segment end for a general ith field-free atom. Then, the *effective* number of field-free atoms per unit length in the segment is

$$\xi = Q'/S = \sum_{i=1}^{Q} 1/f_i \Big/ S \qquad (4.47)$$

and
$$\Delta s_p = \xi x d_1 \qquad (4.48)$$

The results can be easily extended to two-dimensional sheets or three-dimensional blocks of volume SWT. From Eq. 4.48, load–deformation relations can be obtained by inserting the appropriate expressions for x in terms of the force per atom, F. We cannot, however, expect that the number of field-free atoms, Q, will remain constant; instead, Q will increase with F. The extent of crystal defect structure (dislocations) which leads to the occurrence of field-free atoms is known to increase with applied load,[10] so that it can be surmised from experiment that

$$\xi = Q/S = g(F) \qquad (4.49)$$

It is also possible, however, to derive an exact expression for the number of field-free atoms per unit length as a function of the force per atom. In order to do this, we again consider a lattice segment with a single field-free particle present. As a result of a uniform force, F, applied to each atom, the field-free particle will travel a certain distance, x, along the lattice as a particle momentum wave, according to all of our previous remarks. While the particle travels as a wave, it is convenient at this point to consider that its motion is equivalent to that of a particle traveling a distance, x, in a force field, F. Such a particle will then acquire an energy, Fx, in addition to its original energy, $F p d$, and will be capable of creating a new interlattice (field-free) particle whenever x reaches a particular value, x_f, such that

$$F x_f = u_f \qquad (4.50)$$

where u_f is defined as the formation energy for an interlattice atom; that is, the energy required to form a vacancy–interlattice pair, for example, in the middle of the lattice. The total number of field-free particles, q_f, created by a single particle wave moving any distance, x, will be

$$Fx = q_f u_f \tag{4.51}$$

and hence the number created per unit length in the segment is

$$\frac{q_f}{x} = \frac{F}{u_f} \tag{4.52}$$

If there are Q_0 field-free particles originally present in the segment, instead of only one, then each will produce additional field-free particles during propagation along the lattice and, in general, we can write

$$dQ = Q_0 \frac{F}{u_f} dx \tag{4.53}$$

where dQ is the additional number of field-free particles created by Q_0 field-free particles travelling a distance, dx, along the lattice. Integration of Eq. 4.53 gives

$$Q = Q_0 \left(1 + \frac{F}{u_f} x\right) \tag{4.54}$$

from which we can write the expression for the number of field-free atoms per unit length in any segment of length $x = S$ as

$$\frac{Q}{S} = \xi = \xi_0 \left(1 + \frac{FS}{u_f}\right) \tag{4.55}$$

By means of Eq. 4.55, we are now in a position to calculate the shift per unit length, $\Delta s_p/S$, of a lattice segment of arbitrary length, S, from substitution of ξ in Eq. 4.48

$$\Delta s_p = \xi_0 \left(1 + \frac{FS}{u_f}\right) d_1 x \tag{4.56}$$

so that

$$\epsilon_p = \frac{\Delta s_p}{S} = \left(\frac{\xi_0}{S} + \xi_0 \frac{F}{u_f}\right) d_1 x \tag{4.57}$$

and by introducing the previously derived expressions for the dependence of x on F we get

$$\epsilon_p = \left(\frac{\xi_0}{S} + \xi_0 \frac{F}{u_f} \right) \frac{2d_1^2}{\bar{p}} \left[\frac{b\sqrt{F_{pq}}}{\sin b\sqrt{F_{pq}}} \right]^4 \qquad (4.58)$$

$$F_{p1} \leq F \leq F_1$$

$$\epsilon_p = \xi_0 \frac{m}{u_f} \frac{d_1^5 \pi^4}{h^2} \cdot F^2 \qquad (4.59)$$

$$\epsilon_p \geq \epsilon_1; \; F \geq F_1 \qquad \text{and} \qquad F/u_f \gg 1/S$$

The energy, u_f, needed to create a field-free (interlattice) atom can always be written as some fraction of the lattice dissociation energy per atom, $u_f = fD$, and we have already demonstrated that $D = mc_s^2$, so that

$$u_f = fD = fmc_s^2 \qquad (4.60)$$

As a result of substituting this expression for u_f into Eq. 4.59, we see that

$$\epsilon_p = \frac{\xi_0 d_1^5 \pi^4}{fc_s^2 h^2} F^2 \qquad (F > F_1) \qquad (4.61)$$

From Eqs. 4.59 and 4.61, we note especially that above the critical force, F_1 (corresponding to the characteristic velocity, v_1), the relation between force per atom and lattice shift per unit length is parabolic. The parabolic coefficient, furthermore, is independent of the lattice masses and is a function only of the initial number of field-free atoms present per unit length, the lattice spacing, Planck's constant, and the mean sound velocity, c_s, previously defined.

These results for a one-dimensional lattice segment of arbitrary length, S, can be applied to three-dimensional crystals by considering particle-wave motion through a particular lattice segment in a crystal to result in a shift or flow of the segment relative to the crystal, as shown in Figure 4.11a. Here is a cross-sectional diagram showing in a crude way how, in compression, atoms from the loaded ends of the sample "flow" or shift to the sides as a result of particle-wave propagation in the slip directions with spacing, d_1. We see that Δs_p does not represent an extension of a lattice segment; rather, a uniform force applied to the segment produces an effective translation of the segment, as atoms from the loaded ends first shift to interlattice positions and then travel to the opposite segment end on the free lateral surface. After "deformation," an individual segment may have the same length, S, but is now shifted an amount, Δs_p, relative to its original position. In tension, atoms from the sides flow toward the ends, as illustrated in Figure 4.11b. In both cases, the newly formed portion of the crystal is built up by shifts of atoms from the vanishing region, according to the force–shift laws previously given. Layers of "new" crystal form somewhat in the manner of Chinese checkers as

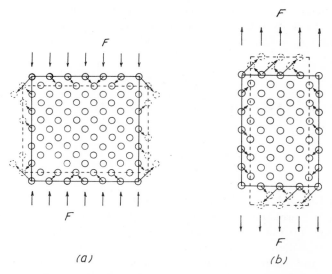

(a)   (b)

Fig. 4.11. (a) Diagram showing how a "flow" or shift of atoms along slip directions (in this case, at 45° from sample faces) leads to deformation of a crystal block in compression. New positions of atoms are indicated by arrows and dashed circles. Material from the ends of the specimen is transferred to the sides in compression at constant volume. (b) Diagram showing how a "flow" or shift of atoms along slip directions (45° lines) leads to deformation of a crystal block in extension. New positions of atoms are indicated by arrows and dashed circles. Material from the sides of the specimen is transferred to the ends in extension at constant volume.

particle-waves propagate through the new regions during their formation. Of course, it is not necessary to imagine that individual atoms actually diffuse or migrate from one part of the crystal to another; only a *momentum* displacement is needed to propagate a particle wave; the "particle" can be said to be where the momentum is, however, and it is the *momentum* displacement, x, which we have called the particle-wave displacement. As a result of this momentum propagation, each atom along a segment is shifted into an adjoining lattice site to accomplish the eventual translation of an entire segment.

The extent of shift, Δs_{pi}, of each segment or lattice row depends on the length, S_i; longer segments shift a greater distance than short ones, so that an effective rotation must really take place for uniform loading of each segment through rigid grips. This is shown schematically in Figure 4.12 for both compression and tension. In compression, the slip direction (direction of closest spacing) will rotate toward the axial external-stress direction near the loading grips, while in tension, the rotation near the grips will tend to move the original slip direction away from alignment with the specimen (and load) axis. The rotation of the central section of the specimen (at large distances from the loaded ends) will, in each case, be opposite to that near the grips; that is, the slip direction will move toward the load direction in tension and away from the load direction in compression.

The expression relating F and Δs_p for an individual segment (Eq. 4.56) can be written in terms of a normal stress, Y_0, and the change in length, ΔL, for the samples pictured in the preceding figures. Consider a particular atom site on the surface of the compression sample, as shown in Figure 4.13. The change in length, ΔL, which occurs directly under this spot will result from atomic shifts, Δs_i, of segments, S_i, in the n available slip directions, each with orientation factor, Ω_i, relative to the normal force per atom, F_0, applied at the point,

$$\Delta L = \sum_{i=1}^{n} \Delta L_i = \sum_{i=1}^{n} \Delta s_i \Omega_i \qquad (4.62)$$

where $\Omega_i = \cos \alpha_i \cos \beta_i$, as previously defined. We also note that the segment length, S_i, from the loaded end to the free surface of the sample, will depend jointly on the sample length, the orientation, and the location of the segment end on the loaded face. For a particular location

$$O_iL = S_i\Omega_i \qquad (4.63)$$

where O_i is a factor depending on the sample shape, so that

$$\epsilon_{Li} = \frac{\Delta L_i}{L} = O_i \frac{\Delta s_i}{S_i} = O_i\epsilon_{pi} \qquad (4.64)$$

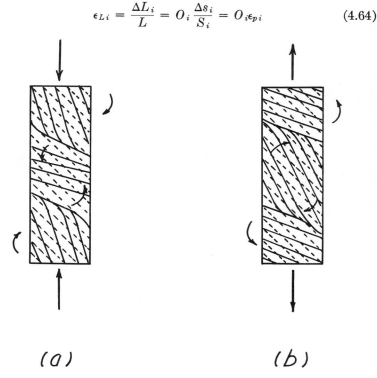

(a)   (b)

Fig. 4.12. (a) Diagram showing rotations that take place in a loaded crystal specimen in compression (rigid grips) as a result of unequal shifts of lattice segments of different overall lengths. Near grips, slip direction rotates toward the specimen (load) axis, but, in the center of the specimen, rotation is *away* from the load axis. Original slip direction is shown by dashed lines. (b) Diagram showing rotations that take place in a loaded crystal specimen in tension (rigid grips) as a result of unequal shifts of lattice segments of different overall lengths. Near grips, slip direction rotates away from the load direction, but, in the center of the specimen, rotation is toward the load axis. Original slip direction is shown by dashed lines.

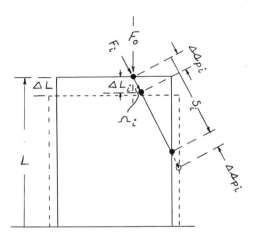

Fig. 4.13. Diagram showing the shift, Δs_{pi}, produced in a lattice segment, S_i, as a result of force component, $F_i = F_0\Omega_i$, in the slip direction, as indicated. This lattice-segment shift contributes an amount, ΔL_i, to the axial change in length, ΔL, of the specimen.

To obtain ϵ_{Li} as a function of applied normal stress, Y_0, it is only necessary to recall that

$$F_i = Y_0\, \Omega_i/\zeta \tag{4.65}$$

where ζ = number of atoms per cross-sectional area, and substitute in Eqs. 4.58 and 4.61 previously given for ϵ_p

$$\epsilon_{Li} = \left(\frac{\xi_0\Omega_i}{L} + \frac{O_i\xi_0 Y_0\Omega_i}{\zeta f c_s^2 m}\right)\frac{2d_i^2}{\bar{p}}\left[\frac{a\sqrt{Y_{0q}\Omega_i}}{\sin a\sqrt{Y_{0q}\Omega_i}}\right]^4 \tag{4.66}$$

$$Y_{p1} \leq Y_0\Omega_i \leq Y_1$$

$$\epsilon_{Li} = \frac{O_i\xi_0 d_1^5\pi^4}{\zeta^2 f c_s^2 h^2}\,(Y_0\Omega_i)^2 \tag{4.67}$$

$$Y_0\Omega_i > Y_1$$

$$a = \frac{d_1}{h}\sqrt{\frac{\bar{p}d_1 m}{2\zeta}}$$

These relations give the resolved shear-strain (ϵ_{Li}) shear-stress ($Y_0\Omega_i$) relations in the direction Ω_i at a particular spot, but can be extended to give the mean strain, $\bar{\epsilon}_{Li}$, over the sample face by substitution of a mean value, $\bar{O}_i$, for the sample-location orientation factor. From its definition, it is clear that $\bar{O}_i$ may depend on sample shape and size, as well as orientation.

If the elastic contribution is added, then the total, general resolved-shear stress–shear strain curve will appear, as shown in Figure 4.14.

(1) Below the limiting stress, Y_{p1}, only elastic deformation occurs. The value of Y_{p1} depends inversely on the segment lengths into which the crystal is divided by existing substructure.

$$Y_{p1} = \frac{\zeta h^2}{8\bar{p}m\boldsymbol{d}_1 S^2} \qquad (4.68)$$

(2) Above Y_{p1}, particle-wave deformation or flow is added to the elastic deformation, and a low-slope region or plateau occurs in the curve. The width or extent of this plateau will vary primarily according to

$$\epsilon_{L0} = 2\xi_0\boldsymbol{d}_1^2\Omega_i/\bar{p}L \qquad (4.69)$$

and hence will vary with ξ_0, the orientation, Ω_i, and inversely with sample length and the field-free distance parameter, $\bar{p}$. Since ξ_0 represents the original number of field-free particles present, the plateau width can be increased by increasing the number of inter-lattice atoms present, for example. The plateau width should also increase with decreasing L. The effect of orientation should result in maximum width for largest values of Ω_i; that is, for central orientations with respect to the standard stereographic triangle.

(3) The slope of the next region, and, to a lesser extent, its width, depends on a term

$$M = 2\boldsymbol{d}_1^2 O_i\xi_0/\zeta f\boldsymbol{c}_s^2\bar{p}m \qquad (4.70)$$

This term will depend on the initial number of field-free atoms present, together with orientation, in a complicated way through $\bar{O}_i$ and ζ. Thus, if the cross-sectional surface changes from one of low to high atomic density, the slope will decrease and the apparent width

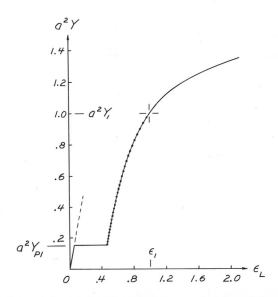

Fig. 4.14. General shape of stress–strain curve for a crystal, according to the particle-wave view of non-elastic deformation and Eqs. 4.66 and 4.67 of the text. Below the elastic limit stress, Y_{p1}, only elastic strains appear, but above Y_{p1}, both continuous elastic and discrete particle-wave contributions occur; above the characteristic stress, Y_1, the particle-wave strain is continuous and a parabolic stress–strain law prevails. The elastic-limit stress varies inversely as the substructure segment length squared, and Y_1 depends on Planck's constant, the crystal spacing, atomic mass, and a field-free parameter, $\bar{p}$, as discussed in the text. The width of the strain plateau depends on sample length, orientation, and defect state, as defined by both $\bar{p}$ and the number of field-free atoms per unit length, ξ_0; a is a constant dependent on crystal spacing and atomic constants.

increase, but the shape-orientation factor, O_i, will also change and might compensate.

(4) As the value of resolved stress, $Y_0\Omega_i$, increases a rise in the stress–strain curve occurs beyond the plateau region, followed by a region of decreasing slope. The initial rise may be nearly linear for particular values of M, but as the stress approaches Y_1, the curve becomes more nearly parabolic. In this region of the curve, discrete jumps may be observed at slow loading rates.

(5) Above Y_1, the stress–strain curve proceeds smoothly according to a parabolic relation

$$(Y_0\Omega_i)^2 = \beta^2 \epsilon_{Li} \tag{4.71}$$

where the coefficient β^2 is given by

$$\beta^2 = \frac{\zeta^2 f c_s^2 h^2}{O_i \xi_0 d_1^5 \pi^4} \tag{4.72}$$

or

$$\beta = \sqrt{\frac{f}{O_i \xi_0}} \cdot \frac{\zeta h c_s}{\pi^2 d_1^{5/2}} \tag{4.73}$$

The fraction of dissociation energy needed to create a field-free atom should be about one-third because such an atom breaks loose from only one of its three vibrational modes (destroys one phonon) in moving to an interlattice position; in any case, f will be very nearly the same for all cubic metals. However, the number of atoms per cross-sectional area, ζ, will depend on the lattice spacing for crystals of the same class. Hence, variations in the parabolic coefficient between metals of the same structure should depend primarily on their relative lattice spacings, sound velocities, and the initial number of field-free atoms per cm present in the slip directions.

6. COMPARISON WITH EXPERIMENTAL STRESS–STRAIN RESULTS

The experimental facts on stress–strain results are too well known to require elaborate description here. The idealized form of experimental stress–strain curves is indeed like that obtained from Eqs. 4.66 and 4.67 and shown in Figure 4.14. Such a typical curve is given in Figure 4.15. The plastic part of the curve is usually divided,[11] like Gaul,[12] into three parts, sometimes called stage I, stage II, and stage III. This division has caused many to infer the existence of three quite distinct or different processes to account for each portion of the curve. This, in turn, has led quite naturally to specialization, in which certain groups study only stage I, others only stage II, and so on. From time to time, interdisciplinary conferences may, of course, be arranged between the various workers to avoid discontinuities where sections of the curve join. Recently, another group[13] has discovered that the curved stage III portion can be fitted quite well by a number of straight-line segments, and specialized research teams will soon be formed to study these stage IV, V, etc. regions of the curve.

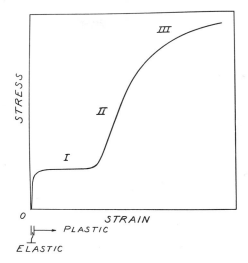

Fig. 4.15. Idealized experimental stress–strain curve of a face-centered cubic crystal showing regions of elastic and plastic strain. The plastic region is usually subdivided into three regions for analysis, as shown. Note the close resemblance between this idealized experimental curve and the stress–strain law given in Figure 4.14.

The particle-wave view of deformation leads to explicit, stress–strain relations for the entire stress–strain curve; a single process—that of particle-wave propagation—accounts for the curve without recourse to Caesarean or other sectioning. The effects of orientation, sample size, the occurrence of steps or jumps in slow loading tests, and other aspects of the observed results, are provided for in the particle-wave stress–strain laws just given.

Some experimental data of Pond and Harrison[14] are shown in Figure 4.16 for single and bicrystals of aluminum tested in compression. The samples were only ⅜-in. long, and a well-defined low plateau or foot is seen in these curves.

An explicit test of the particle-wave stress–strain law is provided by some of Green's results,[15] shown in Figure 4.17. These are nominal stress–strain data in compression for single-crystal aluminum samples of the same orientation and diameter, but varying lengths. In this case, the elastic-limit stress was virtually zero, but the plateau did vary inversely with $1/L$, as it should according to Eq. 4.69. All samples were taken from the same crystal, so that the only variable

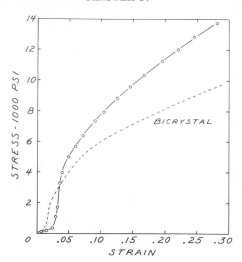

Fig. 4.16. Stress–strain curve for an aluminum single crystal (99.99+%) tested in compression. Notice initial low-slope region or plateau extending to about 0.025 strain. Results for a bicrystal of aluminum are indicated by the dashed line. Samples were ⅛ × ⅛ × ⅜ in. long. From data of Pond and Harrison.[14]

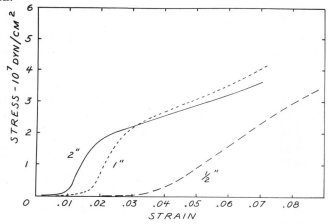

Fig. 4.17. Stress–strain curves for aluminum single crystals tested in compression showing effect of changes in specimen length, as indicated. All samples were ½-in. diameter, of identical axial orientation, and taken from the same crystal. The results were obtained in an Instron machine operated at a crosshead velocity of 3.3 × 10⁻⁴ cm/sec. From data of Green.[15] The initial strain foot is seen to increase as the specimen length decreases.

was L. The results of tensile tests on standard ASTM polycrystalline samples of aluminum, copper, and steel are shown next, in Figures 4.18–4.20. These data were obtained by Glass and Pond[16] from moving picture frames of the samples taken during the test; there was no preloading of the sample. The initial portions of these curves (prior to necking) are again in general agreement with the particle-wave predictions. The appearance of steps or jumps in stress–strain curves of 2S aluminum tested in torsion has been reported by Dillon[17] who, in very slow loading tests, gets results like those shown in Figure 4.21.

Other factors which influence the strain plateau are temperature, impurities, and pretest conditioning. These will change ξ_0, or $\bar{p}$, to produce the observed changes in the initial part of the curve. Thus, both quenching and x-irradiation increase the plateau length[18,19]; both of these treatments will obviously increase ξ_0 (field-free or interlattice

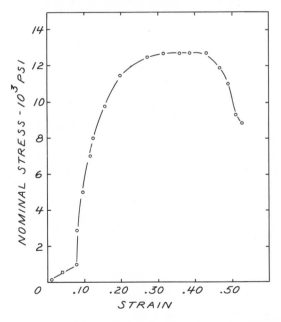

Fig. 4.18. Stress–strain curve for polycrystalline aluminum tested in tension at a straining rate of 0.0625/sec. This was a standard ASTM (E8-46) sample, 2-in. long and 0.505-in. diameter. Strains were obtained from measurements, on moving picture frames, of the sample taken during the test, and there was no preloading of the sample. From data of Glass and Pond.[16]

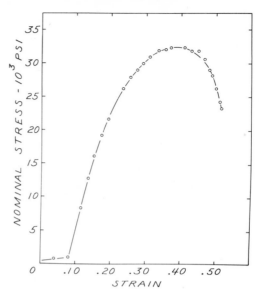

Fig. 4.19. Stress–strain curve for polycrystalline copper tested in tension at a straining rate of 0.0625/sec. A standard ASTM (E8-46) sample, 1-in. long and 0.505-in. diameter, was tested. Strains were obtained from measurements on moving picture frames of the sample taken during the test, and there was no preloading of the sample. From data of Glass and Pond.[16]

particles per cm), and hence, the observed behavior agrees with that predicted from the particle-wave stress–strain curve. A decrease in temperature will decrease $\bar{p}$ as a result of lattice contractions; hence, the plateau should increase in extent as the temperature is lowered. Again, this is the experimental result actually found.[20–22]

Many of the changes which effect the early portion of the stress–strain curve will not vary the parabolic coefficient of the high stress–strain range, but changes in ξ_0 will have an effect on β, according to Eq. 4.73.

Conclusions

By considering the connection between external mechanical load or stress on a crystal, and internally generated particle waves, force–velocity and stress–velocity relations are derived for internal field-free particles. As a result, a force-displacement law for particle waves can be developed by analogy with the dynamic definition of force constant for elastic waves, and this, in turn, leads to a stress–

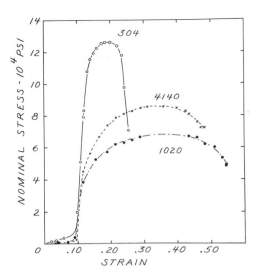

Fig. 4.20. Tensile stress–strain curves for various types of steel, as indicated. Testing procedure was that described for Figures 4.18 and 4.19 and in the text. The 304 stainless steel was cold-rolled and tested at a straining rate of 0.0625/sec. Both the 1020 and 4140 samples were annealed and tested at a straining rate of only 0.00082/sec. From data of Glass and Pond.[16]

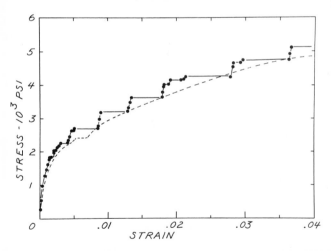

Fig. 4.21. Torsional stress–strain curves for 2S polycrystalline aluminum (annealed for 2 hr. at 1100°F) during extremely slow loading (about 0.01/week). Tubes with an o.d. of ½ in., i.d. of ⅜ in., and length of 9 in. were used. Dashed curve shows results obtained for moderate loading rates. From data of Dillon.[17]

strain law in general agreement with many, if not all, of the observed results for metal polycrystals and single crystals. The initial portion of the stress–strain curve (sometimes called stage I and stage II) depends on a number of parameters which are not present in the expression defining the parabolic coefficient governing the later portion of the curve (stage III), but both parts of the curve will depend on the initial number of field-free atoms per unit length present in the sample at the start of a test.

The derived force–velocity relation for field-free particles leads to an explicit expression for the load dependence of the characteristic particle-wave frequencies, which cause resonances in vibration tests. The sharpness of observed audio-frequency resonances and the possibility of a common frequency for different materials is also explained in terms of applied static loads, rather than particular distributions of lattice segment lengths.

In contrast to the situation for characteristic frequencies and velocities of deformation, exact numerical calculations of stress–strain parameters are not immediately possible. This results from a lack of knowledge concerning the internal field-free distance parameter, p, and the initial number of field-free atoms per unit length, ξ_0. An additional difficulty is that the formation energy for an interlattice field-free atom, u_f, is not known exactly; that is, u_f will be some fraction of the lattice-dissociation energy, fD, but the precise value of f may vary. It is possible, however, to determine both p and ξ_0 from auxiliary measurements, such as the foot length, ϵ_{L0}, of a stress–strain curve and the load dependence of a characteristic frequency. Furthermore, a direct calculation of the *ratios* of average parabolic coefficients for different materials can be made, and these ratios agree well with experimentally observed ratios, as will be shown in Chapter VI.

Some of the results and ideas brought forth in developing the general form of stress–strain laws for crystals have broader implications, which are discussed in Chapter VI.

REFERENCES

1. E. Schmid and W. Boas, *Plasticity of Crystals*, Hughes, London, 1950, Chap. V.
2. G. Sachs, *Z. d. Ver. Deut. Ing.*, **72**, 734–740 (1928); also cited by A. H. Cottrell, *Dislocations and Plastic Flow in Crystals*, Oxford University Press, Oxford, England, 1956, p. 116.

3. G. I. Taylor, *J. Inst. Metals*, **62**, 307–317 (1938); *S. Timenshenko Anniversary Volume*, Macmillan, New York, 1938, p. 218.
4. J. F. W. Bishop and R. Hill, *Phil. Mag.*, **42**, 414–427 (1951); **42**, 1298–1307 (1951).
5. E. R. Fitzgerald, *Phys. Letters*, **10**, 42–43 (1964).
6. J. F. Bell, *Stress Waves in Anelastic Solids*, H. Kolsky and W. Prager, Eds., Springer-Verlag, Berlin, 1963, p. 179; J. F. Bell and J. Suckling, *Proc. 4th Natl. Congr. Appl. Mech., Berkeley*, 877–883 (1962).
7. J. F. Bell, *Proc. Int. Union Theor. Appl. Mech., 1962*, pp. 173–186, Pergamon, New York, 1962.
8. G. I. Taylor, *Proc. Roy. Soc. London*, **A145**, 362–387 (1934); **A145**, 388–406 (1934).
9. J. F. Bell, *J. Appl. Phys.*, **32**, 1982–1993 (1961); *Phil. Mag.*, **10**, 107–126 (1964).
10. A. H. Cottrell, *The Mechanical Properties of Matter*, Wiley, New York, 1964.
11. J. Diehl, S. Mader, and A. Seeger, *Z. Metallk.*, **46**, 650–661 (1955); A. Seeger, *Dislocations and Mechanical Properties of Crystals*, Wiley, New York, 1957, p. 243.
12. J. Caesar, *De Bello Gallico*, Bibracte, Rome, 51 B.C.
13. S. Mader, A. Seeger, and C. Leitz, *J. Appl. Phys.*, **34**, 3368–3375 (1963).
14. R. B. Pond and E. Harrison, *Trans. Am. Soc. Metals*, **50**, 994–1005 (1958).
15. R. E. Green, Jr., private communication.
16. C. M. Glass and R. B. Pond, private communication.
17. O. W. Dillon, Jr., *J. Mech. Phys. Solids*, **11**, 289–304 (1963).
18. C. A. Stearns, A. E. Pack, and R. A. Lad, NASA TN D-75 (Washington, D. C., 1959); *J. Appl. Phys.*, **31**, 231–234 (1960).
19. L. M. Clarebrough and M. E. Hargreaves, *Progr. Metal Phys.*, **8**, 1–103 (1959).
20. J. Garstone, R. W. K. Honeycomb, and G. Greetham, *Acta Met.*, **4**, 485–494 (1956).
21. E. N. Andrade and D. A. Aboav, *Proc. Roy. Soc. London*, **A240**, 304–320 (1957).
22. T. S. Noggle and J. S. Koehler, *J. Appl. Phys.*, **28**, 53–62 (1957).

V

SLIDING FRICTION

Introduction

So far, we have considered various mechanical phenomena concerned with static or dynamic deformations which may occur throughout a crystalline solid as a result of certain loading conditions. Our success in treating these matters leads us next to consider the possibility that the particle momentum-wave view might contribute some understanding to mechanical surface interactions between solids, such as, for example, those occurring in sliding friction. The frictional process is clearly of a dissipative or non-elastic type in which energy is irrecoverably lost as heat, and, in this respect at least, resembles the process of internal slip or plastic deformation in crystals; that is, conservation of momentum is expected, not conservation of energy. We are also tempted by the fact that an adequate explanation of external solid friction has been lacking since Amontons stated his basic law[1] in 1699. This was only fourteen years after the appearance of Hooke's anagram on elasticity, which, in turn, tempts us beyond all caution to set forth the correct explanation of sliding friction in the manner of Hooke, according to the following Latin anagram:

A A A A A C C C C D D E E E E E F G I I I I I I I I
J L L M M M N N N N N O O O R R R R R
S S S S S S S S T T T T T T T U U U U U U U V X

None but the slowest readers will have to wait three years for the solution in this instance, however, as it is presented in Section 2 of this chapter.

1. GENERAL REMARKS ON FRICTION

The chief experimental fact of sliding friction is set forth in terms of the relation between the normal surface force, W, exerted on one solid body by another, and the tangential force, F, needed to start

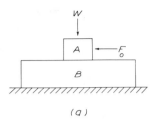

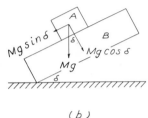

Fig. 5.1. Coefficient of static friction, μ, for block A sliding on B, is given by (a) the horizontal force, F_0, to just start motion divided by the normal force, W, or (b) the tangent of the angle of tilt, δ, at which block A just begins to slide on B.

relative motion or sliding along the surfaces in contact. Thus, if a small block, A, with mass, M, is placed in contact with a larger block, B, as shown in Figure 5.1a, it is found that there will be a minimum tangential force, F_0, needed to just initiate sliding given by

$$F_0 = \mu W \tag{5.1}$$

(Law of Amontons)

where μ is called the coefficient of static friction, as first stated by Amontons[1] in 1699. The value of F_0 needed to start sliding thus is directly proportional to the normal force, W, pressing the two blocks together, and is independent of the area of contact. The value of μ was observed by Amontons to increase with the roughness of the sliding surfaces, but to decrease for greased surfaces. According to Amontons, the value of μ for greased surfaces was independent of the materials of which the blocks were made. Values of μ of about $\frac{1}{3}$ were given by Amontons for ungreased (dry) surfaces. It is possible to find

μ by arranging to tilt block B with respect to the horizontal, as shown in Figure 5.1b. For a given angle of tilt, δ, the normal and tangential surface forces are (as a result of the vertical force of gravity, Mg, acting downward on A) given by

$$F = Mg \sin \delta$$

$$W = Mg \cos \delta$$

so that if the angle of tilt, δ_0, is found at which A just begins to slide along B, then

$$\mu = \frac{F}{W} = \tan \delta_0 \tag{5.2}$$

and μ is determined from a measurement of δ_0, sometimes called the "maximum angle of repose" or simply the "angle of repose."

After sliding has started, it is also found that a certain minimum tangential force, F_0', is needed to maintain the velocity constant at any given value; for unlubricated surfaces this force is lower than that needed to start the motion, but still varies directly as the normal force, W. This leads to the definition of a coefficient of *kinetic* friction, μ', such that

$$F_0' = \mu'W \tag{5.3}$$

Values of μ' may be almost constant for a certain range of velocities, but are generally observed to drop as the velocity increases; at very low velocities, values of μ' rise to approach μ. The variation of μ' with sliding velocity for dry (unlubricated) solids is roughly as shown in Figure 5.2 in many cases.[2,3] Coefficients of static friction for pure metals often reach values of 2 to 5, or even higher,[4,5] when the sliding surfaces are thoroughly decontaminated or outgassed by heating in a vacuum to temperatures just below melting. In fact, in some cases when carefully prepared metal surfaces are placed together in a vacuum, "seizure" occurs corresponding to infinite values of μ. On the other hand, the velocity dependence of the coefficient of friction for surfaces "contaminated" by the presence of impurities, oxides, or lubricants is generally less pronounced, and the frictional coefficients are reduced to values of the order of 0.5 to 0.1 or less.

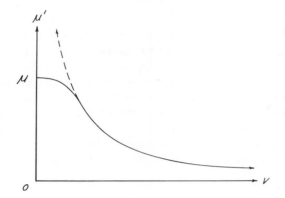

Fig. 5.2. Typical variation of the coefficient of kinetic friction, μ', with sliding velocity, v, found under ordinary conditions for solid bodies sliding in air (solid line). Dashed line at low velocities indicates rapid rise in μ' found for clean solids sliding in a vacuum.

Explanations advanced to account for the occurrence of sliding friction usually consider the sliding surfaces to consist of a series of interlocking protuberances which exist on a microscopic scale even for carefully polished specimens, as shown in Figure 5.3. Thus, Parent[6] in 1700 explained Amontons' results in terms of surfaces studded with rigid hemispherical bosses, so that a tangential force was required to slide one set of bosses out of the troughs and onto the tops of the others. Similarly, Coulomb[7] in 1785 attributed sliding friction to the work necessary to lift two bodies over their respective surface asperities, which could also deform elastically. Later explanations, such as those of Hardy[8] and Thomlinson[9] in 1919 and 1929, respectively, have attributed friction to atomic or molecular adhesion,

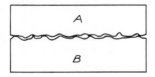

Fig. 5.3. Cross-sectional view of two solids in sliding contact, showing the surface irregularities (asperities) which result in frictional sliding resistance according to the generally accepted view. Welding or strong adhesion may also occur at sharp projections according to Bowden,[2] as indicated by the darkened contact points in this diagram.

while Schurnmann[10] emphasized the importance of contact electricity in 1940. More recently, Bowden[2,11] has proposed a combination of local adhesion and penetration or ploughing-out of grooves in the sliding surfaces. Bowden's explanation thus combines molecular adhesion or local welding at points in contact with the idea of interlocking asperities. These latter, however, are now assumed to undergo plastic deformation in addition to the elastic deformation proposed by Coulomb. Various deficiencies and objections are associated with all of these "theories," as very recently described by Braithwaite,[12] so that a satisfactory explanation of sliding friction has not previously existed.

2. Particle-Wave View of Sliding Friction

In order to see how the particle-wave view of mechanical deformation may be applied to sliding friction, it will be convenient to first recall refraction effects for waves in general. By refraction, of course, we mean the change of direction or bending of a plane wave, for example, which occurs when it crosses the boundary between two media in which the wave velocities differ, as indicated in Figure 5.4a. In general, both a reflected and a refracted wave occur at such a boundary, as indicated by the rays (normals to the wave-fronts) in the figure. The angle of reflection, r, is of course equal to the angle of incidence, i, and the angle, θ, between the refracted ray and the normal to the interface is obtained from Snell's law

$$\frac{\sin i}{\sin \theta} = \frac{v_a}{v_b} \tag{5.4}$$

$$\sin \theta = \frac{v_b}{v_a} \sin i \tag{5.4'}$$

where v_a and v_b are the wave velocities in the media a and b, respectively, as indicated in Figure 5.4. If the incoming wave approaches the boundary at grazing incidence (i.e., at $i = 90°$), the refracted wave reaches its maximum angle, θ_c, as shown in Figure 5.4b. This *critical* angle is given by setting $\sin i = 1$ in Eq. 5.4', to give

$$\sin \theta_c = \frac{v_b}{v_a}$$

or

$$\theta_c = \arcsin \left(v_b/v_a\right) \tag{5.5}$$

where

$$v_b \leq v_a$$

We next turn to an idealized case, as shown in Figure 5.5a, where a single atom slides at constant velocity along the surface of an infinitely large cubic crystal of spacing, d. From our particle-wave point of view, the sliding atom represents a particle momentum wave packet striking the boundary between an external field-free medium, a, and the crystal medium, b. Thus, in accordance with our previous remarks about waves in general, there will be a refracted wave at angle θ_c in the crystal as shown, where

$$\theta_c = \arcsin \left(v_b/v_a\right) \tag{5.5}$$

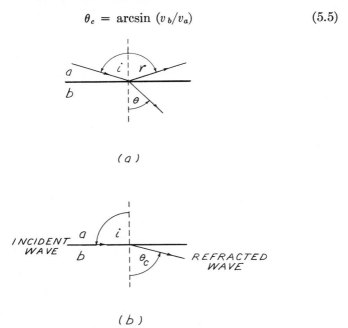

(a)

(b)

Fig. 5.4. (a) Diagram showing how the incident wave from medium a, at angle i from the normal between boundary of material a and material b, is partly reflected and partly refracted into medium b. (b) Diagram showing the incoming wave (ray) at grazing incidence ($i = 90°$) and the refracted wave at the critical angle, θ_c.

where v_a is the wave velocity of the particle wave in the field-free medium, a, and v_b is the wave velocity of the refracted particle wave in the crystal medium, b.

The presence of this refracted momentum wave in the crystal subjects atoms in the crystal to a force whose tangential and normal components, F_0' and W, must be such that their resultant direction coincides with that of the refracted wave, as shown in Figure 5.5b.

$$\mu' = F_0'/W = \tan \theta_c \qquad (5.6)$$

and from Eq. 5.5, we have therefore

$$\mu' = \tan \arcsin (v_b/v_a) \qquad (5.7)$$

Now, a normal force, W, and a tangential force, F_0', applied directly to the sliding atom will necessarily result in a normal force, W, and a

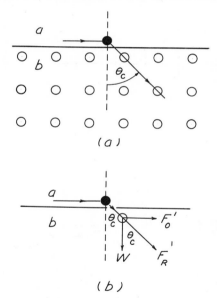

(a)

(b)

Fig. 5.5. (a) Diagram of an atom (filled circle) in region a sliding on the surface of crystal b (open circles), with associated particle-wave rays for the incident grazing wave and the refracted wave at angle θ_c, as indicated. (b) Resolution of the forces which must be exerted on a surface atom in crystal b as a result of the refracted particle momentum wave traveling in direction θ_c in the crystal.

tangential force, F_0', transmitted to the atoms of the crystal over which it slides (since we specify no acceleration of the sliding atom), and thus μ' can be identified as the coefficient of sliding friction for this single atom. Of course, we are really interested in a collection of atoms such as those in the face of block A of Figure 5.1, but, as long as no relative motion takes place within atoms in this block, we can consider its face atoms to be field-free insofar as the block, B, is concerned. Then, a total force, F_0', applied tangentially to the block, A, will produce a tangential force on each atom given by

$$f_T = F_0'/\sigma\zeta$$

where σ is the cross-sectional area of block A in contact with B, and ζ is the number of atoms per unit area. Similarly, a normal force W on A will produce a normal force on each atom in the contact area

$$f_N = W/\sigma\zeta$$

and the ratio of tangential force per atom to normal force per atom is seen to be independent of the area of contact

$$f_T/f_N = F_0'/W$$

Consequently, the macroscopic coefficient of friction for block A sliding on an infinite block B is the same as that for a single atom given in Eq. 5.7

$$\mu' = \tan \arcsin (v_b/v_a) \tag{5.7}$$

Values of μ' can be calculated from a knowledge of the wave velocities, v_a and v_b, which have been determined in Chapter I as functions of the wave vector, k. Before evaluating this ratio, however, we must decide which of the two wave velocities is relevant, since the group velocity, v_g, and the phase velocity, c_p, are different functions of k for particle momentum waves. If each surface atom of block A has associated with it a wave packet, then the packet can be thought of as being made up of a number of superimposed, long wave trains, each of slightly different wavelength. Each of these component waves will move with a different propagation velocity (phase velocity) even in the free space outside the crystal block B, and each will, of course, be refracted a different amount when striking the surface of B at grazing incidence. The group velocity, on the other hand, represents an average velocity for the combined packet or pulse, and by following its direction in space we can keep track of the probable position of the particle. Hence, we choose the group velocity as the relevant velocity, although we cannot be certain that this is correct until we compare the result with experiment. Then we have, for like atoms of mass m in both A and B,

$$v_b = v_g \text{ (crystal)} = \frac{h}{\pi m d} \sin\left(\frac{kd}{2}\right) \cos\left(\frac{kd}{2}\right) \qquad \begin{array}{c}(5.8)\\(1.35)\end{array}$$

$$= \frac{2v_1}{\pi} \sin\left(\frac{\pi}{2}\frac{v}{v_1}\right) \cos\left(\frac{\pi}{2}\frac{v}{v_1}\right) \qquad (5.9)$$

where

$$v_a = v = \frac{\hbar}{m} k \qquad \text{and} \qquad v_1 = h/2md$$

The velocity ratio, v_b/v_a, then can be written in terms of v as

$$v_b/v_a = \frac{\sin\left(\dfrac{\pi}{2}\dfrac{v}{v_1}\right) \cos\left(\dfrac{\pi}{2}\dfrac{v}{v_1}\right)}{\dfrac{\pi}{2}\dfrac{v}{v_1}} \qquad (5.10)$$

and consequently, an expression for the coefficient of sliding friction, μ', can be written as a function of the characteristic velocity, v_1, and the sliding velocity, $v_a = v$

$$\mu' = \tan \arcsin \left[\frac{\sin\left(\dfrac{\pi}{2}\dfrac{v}{v_1}\right) \cos\left(\dfrac{\pi}{2}\dfrac{v}{v_1}\right)}{\left(\dfrac{\pi}{2}\dfrac{v}{v_1}\right)} \right] \qquad (5.11)$$

or, in terms of the lattice masses and spacing, as

$$\mu' = \tan \arcsin \left[\frac{\sin\left(\dfrac{md}{2\hbar}v\right) \cos\left(\dfrac{md}{2\hbar}v\right)}{\left(\dfrac{md}{2\hbar}v\right)} \right] \qquad (5.12)$$

Now we cannot expect to be so fortunate as to have available an infinite crystal block for sliding experiments; even when the block is very large, we expect that its surface will consist of many short lattice segments or mosaics, as discussed previously. For such finite lattice segments of length $S = Nd$, only certain discrete values of the wave vector, k, are allowed

$$k = q\pi/Nd \tag{5.13}$$

$$q = 1, 2, 3 \ldots (N - 1)$$

These restrictions on k also impose similar limits on the allowed values of the group velocity, v_b, in the crystal, and the coefficient of friction will now be limited to values corresponding to only certain sliding velocities

$$v_q = \frac{\hbar}{m} \frac{\pi}{Nd} q \tag{5.14}$$

$$= \frac{h}{2md} \frac{q}{N}$$

$$q = 1, 2, 3 \ldots (N - 1)$$

Eq. 5.11 can therefore be rewritten in terms of v_q as

$$\mu_q' = \tan \arcsin \left[\frac{\sin \left(\frac{\pi}{2} \frac{v_q}{v_1} \right) \cos \left(\frac{\pi}{2} \frac{v_q}{v_1} \right)}{\left(\frac{\pi}{2} \frac{v_q}{v_1} \right)} \right] \tag{5.15}$$

where we recall that $v_1 = h/2md_1$ is the limiting velocity for the stationary lattice in a direction with spacing, d_1. The lowest value of v_q is now not zero, but

$$v_q \text{ (min)} = \frac{h}{m2Nd_1} \tag{5.16}$$

$$= \frac{h}{m(2S)}$$

so that values of μ_q' will start at some high (but finite) value, and drop to some small (but nonzero) value at the maximum velocity

$$v_q \ (\text{max}) \ = \ \frac{h}{2m\boldsymbol{d}_1} \ \frac{N-1}{N} \tag{5.17}$$

$$= \ v_1 \frac{N-1}{N}$$

$$\cong \ v_1 \qquad \text{for large } N$$

The values of sliding velocity, $v \ (v_a)$, of course, can take on any values, but the coefficient of friction will have only the discrete values given by Eq. 5.15, with abrupt changes in μ_q' occurring at certain values, v_q, of the sliding velocity. The expected variations of μ' with sliding velocity for both infinite and finite lattices are shown in Figure 5.6.

The dependence of the coefficient of kinetic friction on sliding velocity, obtained from Eqs. 5.11 or 5.15, is thus seen to agree with the general shape of the experimental μ' vs. v curves, as shown previously in Figure 5.2. Further, we have already noted that μ' should be independent of the area of contact between the sliding bodies, according to the development presented here, and this also is in agreement with experiment. From Eq. 5.15, we can calculate the value of static friction $(\mu' \rightarrow \mu)$ for the lowest possible value of velocity, v_q, as given by Eq. 5.16. In order to do this for an "ordinary" surface, we assume that the segment length, S, is about 10^{-4} cm, in agreement with the experimental evidence already cited[13] in Chapter II. For aluminum, this gives a value of $N = 3.5 \times 10^3$ and

$$v_q \ (\text{min}) \ = \ v_1/N \ = \ (2.585 \times 10^3)/3.5 \times 10^3 \ = \ 0.74 \ \text{cm/sec}$$

Values of the angle in Eq. 5.15 are, correspondingly,

$$\frac{\pi}{2} \frac{v_q}{v_1} = \frac{\pi}{2} \times \frac{1}{N} \cong 0.448 \times 10^{-3} \ \text{radians}$$

$$\cong 0.0256 \ \text{degrees}$$

from which the value of μ', up to $v_q = 0.74$ cm/sec, is

$$\mu' \,(\text{max}) \;=\; \tan \arcsin 0.99999987$$

$$\cong 2000$$

While this value is not infinite, it still leads us to expect a very large value for the coefficient of static friction for clean (unlubricated)

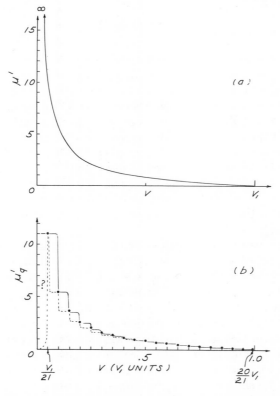

Fig. 5.6. Variation of the coefficient of friction, μ', with velocity, v, for sliding (a) between like monatomic crystals for an infinite lattice, and (b) between like monatomic crystals with a finite lattice, where the length is given by $S = Nd$ and $N = 21$. The lattice spacing is d, and the characteristic velocity, v, is given by $h/2md$, as explained in the text. Possible behavior between the discrete values of velocity is indicated by solid and dashed lines. For the usual case where N is large (~ 3000), the discrete points are much more closely spaced than shown here.

metal surfaces of the same kind. On the other hand, if the surface of the crystal is broken up into smaller lattice segments by severe work hardening or through the introduction of impurity atoms, maximum values of μ' can be expected to drop drastically. For example, if $N = 3.5 \times 10^2$, then

$$\mu' \text{ (max)} \cong 140$$

and if $N = 35$

$$\mu' \text{ (max)} \cong 18$$

etc.

In connection with the effect of surface conditions on the coefficient of friction, we notice that the refracted particle wave, whose group velocity, v_b, determines the value of μ', lies very near the surface for small values of sliding velocity, v, since $v_a = v_b$ for small values of k and v, and $\theta_c = 90°$. Hence, we can expect that changes in the surface structure of the crystal will have profound consequences on the static and low-velocity values of the frictional coefficient. At high velocities, however, the refracted ray bends more sharply into the crystal, approaching the normal to the surface ($\theta_c = 0°$) as the sliding velocity approaches $v_1 = h/2md_1$. Hence, high velocity values of μ' should be insensitive to the surface properties and depend on the bulk properties of the crystal.

Another consequence of high velocity sliding is that the wavelength of the associated particle wave, which is refracted into the crystal, approaches the limiting value of $\lambda = 2d_1$. That is, when the sliding velocity of the "free particle" generating the grazing incident wave approaches the limiting value, $v_1 = h/2md_1$, the wavelength of both the field-free and the crystal particle wave is $\lambda = 2d_1$. As we have already seen in Chapter III, shorter wavelengths can only be propagated if sections of the crystal lattice move *against* such an incoming particle wave. The direction of the refracted ray will continue to be normal to the sliding surface, but, for sliding velocities greater than v_1, we expect a "mushrooming" or flaring-out to occur between blocks of the same width, or "banks" to form around a small block sliding across a larger one. At still higher sliding velocities above the fission velocity, v_f, given by

$$v_f \cong \sqrt{v_1 \cdot c_s} \qquad (5.18)$$
$$(3.29)$$

we expect that disintegration of the crystal lattice will occur, and that craters (grooves) should be formed in the block. At sufficiently high velocities, both the slider and the block will break up. Crystal fragments should be observed flying off from the sliding surface, just as in the case of hypervelocity impact.

So far, we have considered sliding friction between similar materials where the atom mass, m, is the same for both block A and block B, for example. Let us now suppose that block A is formed of a material with atomic mass, m_a, such that

$$m_a = m/r \qquad (5.19)$$

$$r > 1$$

where m and d are the atomic mass and the spacing of block B, as before. The wavelength of the "free" particles of block A sliding at velocity v can then be written in terms of the mass, m, of B as

$$\lambda = \frac{h}{m_a v} = \frac{h}{m \dfrac{v}{r}} \qquad (5.19')$$

and hence, we can consider that the increased wavelength resulting from the new, lighter mass of the incident particle is equivalent to the wavelength resulting from the original mass incident at a slower velocity, v/r. The expression for the group velocity of the particle wave propagating in block B can be written in terms of the characteristic velocity, $v_1 = h/2md_1$, of B as

$$v_b \text{ (group)} = \frac{2}{\pi} v_1 \cdot \sin\left(\frac{\pi}{2} \frac{v}{rv_1}\right) \cos\left(\frac{\pi}{2} \frac{v}{rv_1}\right) \qquad (5.20)$$

while $v_a = v$, so that the expression for the coefficient of friction now becomes

$$\mu' = \tan \arcsin \left[\frac{1}{r} \cdot \frac{\sin\left(\dfrac{\pi}{2} \dfrac{v}{rv_1}\right) \cdot \cos\left(\dfrac{\pi}{2} \dfrac{v}{rv_1}\right)}{\left(\dfrac{\pi}{2} \dfrac{v}{rv_1}\right)} \right] \qquad (5.20')$$

with the result that the value of μ' for a particular value of sliding velocity is greatly reduced, while at the same time, the velocity at which μ' drops to zero is increased. In our previous example of aluminum sliding on aluminum, we recall that μ' was 2000 at a velocity of 0.74 cm/sec, but μ' for aluminum sliding on copper at the same speed becomes

$$\mu = \tan \arcsin \left(\frac{1}{2.35} \right)$$

$$\cong 0.47$$

The expected variation of μ' with velocity for sliding between unlike materials, for a mass ratio of two, is shown in Figure 5.7. In connection with Eq. 5.20', the question naturally rises as to the meaning to be attached to a situation where $r < 1$, i.e., when the atoms of block A are heavier than those of B. At low velocities, such a situation could lead to values of $\sin \theta_c$ greater than one or, in short, circumstances under which the expression for μ' has no meaning. We are saved from this embarrassment in macroscopic or bulk sliding experiments by considering again our original arguments for treating the bottom surface atoms of block A as field-free atoms sliding across the top of B. From the symmetry of the situation, it is at once clear that the top surface atoms of B can also be considered as field-free atoms sliding (in the opposite direction) across the bottom surface of A. Thus, for blocks of identical materials, each "slides" along the other and identical refracted particle waves are present in each block.

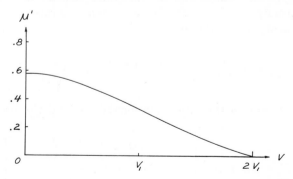

Fig. 5.7. Variation of the coefficient of friction, μ', with sliding velocity between unlike monatomic crystals for an atomic mass ratio of $r = 2.0$.

For dissimilar materials, there will be a range of low velocities where only the light metal can slide along the heavier one; at higher velocities, mutual sliding may become possible, but the frictional coefficients for the two cases will be different, and one form will be predominate. Thus a macroscopic aluminum rider may slide across a copper block with the same coefficient of friction as a copper rider across an aluminum block, but at slow speeds, aluminum atoms are really sliding across copper in both cases.

In view of the dependence of v_1, and thus v_b, on lattice spacing, we also expect that directional effects should occur in sliding friction between two single-crystal blocks or between a polycrystalline block and a single crystal.

The correctness of these (and other) predictions based on the particle-wave explanation of sliding friction will be demonstrated by comparison with experimental results, which are presented in the following section. The dependence of the coefficient of friction on velocity, however, seems to be sufficiently in accord with the general experimental facts on sliding friction to allow us to decipher the anagram[14] given at the beginning of this Chapter, and which the learned will now recognize as the Latin statement of Eq. 5.7:

INDEX FRICTIONIS TANGENS ARCUS CUJUS SINUS
EST RATIO VELOCITATUM UNDORUM MATERIAL

3. Comparison with Experimental Results

One of the principal predictions following from Eqs. 5.12 and 5.15 is that values of the frictional coefficient, μ', at low sliding velocities (i.e., "static" values) should be very high for unlubricated like surfaces. That is, for an infinite lattice, the values of the static frictional coefficient should be infinite; even for finite segments of about 10^{-4} cm in length, values as high as several thousand are predicted. As already mentioned, very high values are indeed found for clean metals and seizure often occurs between clean metals sliding in a vacuum. Thus, Bowden and Hughes[5] and Bowden and Rowe[5] have shown that if separated metal sliders are first heated to produce surface evaporation in a high vacuum, they will subsequently seize together when brought into contact at room temperature, even under small normal loads. This type of investigation was extended by

Rowe,[4] who also studied the effect of reintroducing small quantities of vapor after initial heating or "outgassing" of polycrystalline metal surfaces. Some of Rowe's results are shown in Figure 5.8, where the coefficient of static friction, μ, measured at room temperature, is plotted against "outgassing" temperature. The procedure consisted of heating the metal sliders for 20 minutes in a vacuum of 10^{-2} micro-inches of mercury, and then cooling to room temperature before bringing the sliders (of like metal) together for friction tests. Normal loads from 10 to 20 grams were applied. The results shown in Figure 5.9 are typical of those obtained for copper, iron, silver, chromium, and commercial mild steel. In all of these metals, a steep rise in μ followed heating above about 800°C, with seizure occurring ($\mu \rightarrow \infty$) for higher temperatures after some surface evaporation of the metal. In platinum, however, the steep rise in μ around 1000°C, and subsequent seizure after heating at still higher temperatures, took place without any metal evaporation.

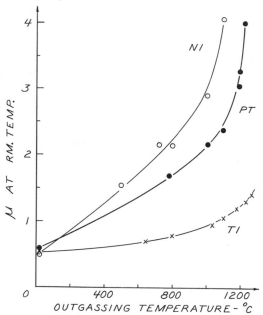

Fig. 5.8. The effect of outgassing temperature on the coefficient of static friction, μ, between like metals subsequently measured in a vacuum at room temperature (from data of Rowe[5]).

Gold, molybdenum, tantalum, zirconium, uranium, and aluminum all showed increases in μ after heating, but did not seize when subsequently brought into contact at room temperature.

While heating these metals to a high temperature in a vacuum undoubtedly has a cleaning effect, as supposed, we cannot fail to emphasize that this heating also constitutes an annealing process which can be expected to have broad metallurgical consequences. The grain size and the subgrain mosaic structure of the metals will also be effected by the heating. The cooling rate and elapsed time at temperature will likewise be important in determining the domain size or substructure dimensions of crystal blocks within grains, as discussed briefly in Chapter II and at length by Hirsch.[13] Thus, from our point of view, the observed changes in the coefficient of friction may arise partly from increases in the length of finite lattice segments resulting from changes in the surface mosaic structure of the metals. Hence, the failure of certain metals to seize may be explained by the short annealing time (20 min.) in which the average substructure size did not have time to grow sufficiently, or by quenching effects from rapid cooling (also 20 min.).

Another result of Rowe's investigation was to show that the introduction of a gas or vapor (e.g., O_2, H_2O, H_2S, I_2, Cl_2) will prevent seizure. Thus, oxygen at pressures above 0.01 atmospheres reduced the friction of pure copper from seizure (∞) to 1.8. When the oxygen gas was subsequently pumped off, the coefficient rose to 2.4, which compares with a maximum value of 2.5 found after severe outgassing of commercially pure copper (i.e., copper containing oxygen). Similar results were found for oxygen gas and silver ($\mu = 1.5$), platinum ($\mu = 1.0$), chromium ($\mu = 1.4$), and other metals. Materials such as titanium showed a slight reduction in μ (e.g., from 1.4 to 0.9) when oxygen was present at room temperature, but since these metals did not seize anyway, the change was less dramatic. The other gases and vapors produced comparable results. From our point of view, of course, the presence of a gas or vapor may prevent seizure by chemisorption or physisorption of the gas molecules on the metal surface, and the consequent changes in lattice spacing which result in the surface layer of atoms, or from atoms of different mass present as impurities on the crystal surface. A compilation of static coefficients of friction has been prepared by Minshall[15] for both clean metals in vacuum and metals in the presence of gases. Gross seizure ($\mu \rightarrow \infty$)

is reported by Minshall for the following clean metals in a vacuum: Al on Al, Cu on Cu, Au on Au, Fe on Fe, Mo on Mo, Ni on Ni, Pt on Pt, and Ag on Ag. On the other hand, in the presence of H_2 or N_2, gas values of μ are: Au, 4.0; Cu, 4.0; Ni, 5.0; while in air or O_2, some values of μ given are: Al, 1.9; Cu, 1.6; Au, 2.8; Fe, 1.2; Mo, 0.8; Ni, 3.0; Pt, 3.0; Ag, 1.5.

A second prediction following from Eq. 5.12 is that values of the sliding friction coefficient should decrease with increasing sliding velocity, as shown in Figures 5.6 and 5.7. We have already mentioned that this is generally true, but will now present some specific data showing such velocity dependence. Some of the earliest measurements showing the effect of velocity on μ' were those of Galton[16] for cast-iron brake blocks on steel wagon wheels, as shown in Figure 5.9. More recently, the variation of μ' at speeds up to about 10^5 cm/sec (2200 mph) has been measured by Freitag[17] and Freitag and Bowden,[18] using the apparatus sketched in Figure 5.10. A hardened steel ball of one-half inch diameter is first suspended in the magnetic field of a

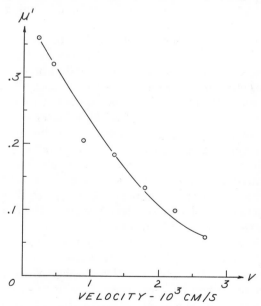

Fig. 5.9. The variation of the coefficient of friction, μ', with sliding velocity, v, for cast-iron brake blocks on steel wheels (from data of Galton[16]).

solenoid, where vertical stability is achieved by a photoelectric feed-back system which controls the current through the solenoid. This freely suspended ball is then accelerated by a rotating magnetic field of constant frequency (22,500 cps) while in a vacuum (10^{-5} cm of Hg).

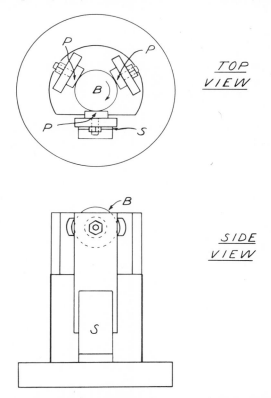

Fig. 5.10. Diagram of Freitag and Bowden's apparatus for the determina-tion of frictional coefficients at high velocities. A hardened steel ball, B, is suspended in the magnetic field of a solenoid (not shown), and accelerated by a rotating magnetic field in a central position between three pads, P, of the specimen or "target" material. The front pad is fastened to a spring, S, and is at first drawn back so that the ball rotates freely, but after the desired velocity is reached, the spring is released and the ball is then pushed into contact with the three pads. From the deceleration of the ball (measured using a photo cell), the tangential frictional force, and thus μ', is deter-mined. The entire apparatus is housed in a vacuum chamber during the test.[17,18]

Surface speeds up to about 1000 m/sec are easily attained; the limit depends on the bursting strength of the steel ball. The rotational speed of the ball is measured by means of marks placed on its polished surface and a photomultiplier cell which picks up reflected light from the surface. The intensity of the reflected light can then be recorded as a function of time to give the angular velocity of the ball; deceleration of the ball resulting from frictional forces can also be measured. After the ball reaches a desired speed, it is brought into contact with three metal pads by releasing a leaf spring on which one of the pads is mounted. As a result of the normal pressure exerted by the spring and the coefficient of friction between the ball and the three pads, a deceleration results in direct proportion to the tangential frictional force, F_0'. By measuring the deceleration, and from a knowledge of the normal force, W, imposed by the spring, values of μ' can be calculated.

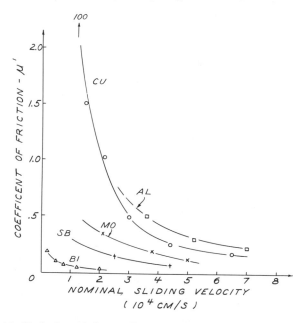

Fig. 5.11. Variation of the coefficient of friction, μ', with velocity for the steel ball of Figure 5.10 against the metals indicated. At low velocities, siezure occurred for aluminum and copper as a result of prior metal transfer from the specimens to the steel ball, as explained in the text (from data of Freitag[17] and Freitag and Bowden[18]).

The metal pads usually consisted of small disks (¼-in. diameter ×
1⁄16-in. thick) screwed into holders.

From our discussion of impact experiments in Chapter III, it must
be evident that the true sliding velocity at impact in this apparatus
may be somewhat less than the measured velocity. That is, the three
metal pads or "targets" are not semi-infinite with respect to the ball;
nor are the holders and the plastic base for the apparatus very
massive. Thus, we cannot expect to obtain quantitative velocity data,
although the trend should be correctly given by the results.

Representative data from the apparatus of Figure 5.10 are shown
in Figure 5.11 for a steel ball sliding on copper, aluminum, bismuth,
antimony, and molybdenum. The results represent the friction
observed just after the ball touched the specimen in each case. Violent
seizure occurred for copper at speeds below about 1.3×10^4 cm/sec,
and for aluminum at speeds of 0.4×10^4 cm/sec. The observed values
of μ' are thus seen to decrease from very high values at low speeds
(μ' is estimated to be 100–200 at 1.3×10^4 cm/sec) to very low values
at high speeds, in perfect agreement with the prediction of Eq. 5.12
or Eq. 5.15. Similar results were also found for other materials
(including polymers) by Bowden and Persson,[19] as shown in Figure
5.12. Miller[20] has also determined the variation of frictional coefficients

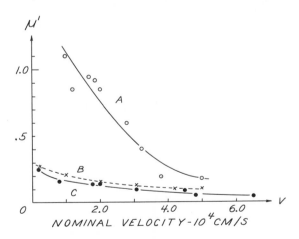

Fig. 5.12. Variation of the coefficient of friction, μ', with velocity for steel
against various polymers: A, Buta-S rubber; B, polytetrafluorethylene; C,
nylon 6-6 (from data of Bowden and Persson[19]).

with velocity for metals sliding on hard crystals, such as sapphire (Al_2O_2), rutile (TiO_2), silicon carbide (SiC), and fused silica (SiO_2). Some of Miller's results are shown in Figure 5.13, where a decrease in μ' with increasing sliding speed is again found.

Of even greater interest to us is the report by Freitag[17] and Freitag and Bowden[18] of a "new and unexpected phenomenon" observed above about 2.5×10^4 cm/sec for bismuth and above 4.0×10^4 cm/sec for antimony. Above these sliding speeds in each case, the surfaces of the metals begin to break up into a fine powder; at still higher speeds, a shower or cloud of fine metal particles fills the vacuum chamber and is so dense that the light beam is cut off, preventing measurements above 3.0×10^4 cm/sec for bismuth and 7.0×10^4 cm/sec for antimony. The ejected metal fragments are not smooth and globular, but, rather, are irregular, often with sharp corners. Individual particles are about 10^{-4} cm in diameter, but sometimes cluster together into larger pieces. Enlarged photographs of some "wear marks" or craters formed by a steel ball sliding against bismuth are presented in Figure 5.14. An enlarged photograph showing similar wear marks or craters formed by a steel ball sliding on copper is adduced in Figure 5.15. These results are, of course, exactly as anticipated by us for sliding velocities above the hypervelocity threshold or the fission velocity, v_f', for steel against each metal. Miller has also noted that steel balls sliding against sapphire produce

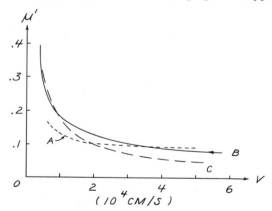

Fig. 5.13. Variation of the coefficient of friction, μ', with velocity for steel against various crystals: A, sapphire (Al_2O_3); B, silicon carbide (SiC); C, titanium carbide (TiC) (from data of Miller[20]).

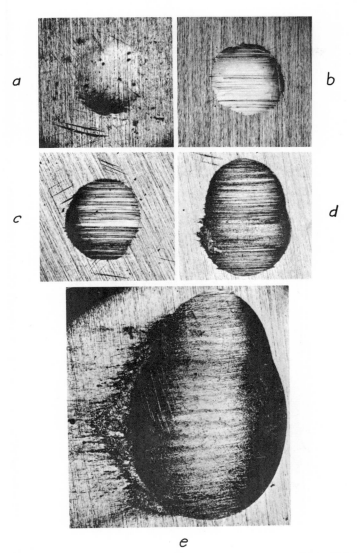

Fig. 5.14. Photographs of wear marks and "craters" formed in bismuth target specimens by a spinning steel ball brought into sliding contact with the specimen at various velocities: a, 0.0×10^4 cm/sec; b, 1.0×10^4 cm/sec; c, 2.0×10^4 cm/sec; d, 3.0×10^4 cm/sec; e, 4.0×10^4 cm/sec. Direction of sliding, right to left. Magnification, $27 \times$. (Photographs by courtesy of F. P. Bowden, University of Cambridge[19]).

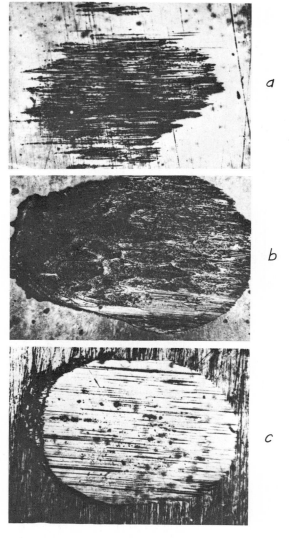

Fig. 5.15. Photographs of wear marks and "craters" formed in copper target specimens by a spinning steel ball brought into sliding contact with the specimens at various velocities: a, 0.01×10^4 cm/sec; b, 1.5×10^4 cm/sec; c, 6.0×10^4 cm/sec. Direction of sliding, right to left. Magnification, $225\times$ (Photographs by courtesy of F. P. Bowden, University of Cambridge[18]).

a cracking of the sapphire which becomes more widespread as the sliding speed increases. Even at 0.80×10^4 cm/sec, some cracks formed, but these became extensive at 5.60×10^4 cm/sec. Frequently, the cracks formed in the sapphire crystal had a preferred direction; the loose debris produced by the sliding was found to consist of both spherical particles of solidified iron and angular blocks of sapphire which had broken off the crystal. Nickel-plated and nickel balls produced even greater damage; the sapphire crystals completely fractured at speeds around 1.20×10^4 cm/sec, so that measurements above this velocity could not be made. Cracking into small blocks was also observed in titanium carbide crystals, which broke up completely above 5.20×10^4 cm/sec when brought into contact with a steel ball.

As we have pointed out before, the size and mass of the "target" pads in the spinning ball apparatus, relative to the size and mass of the ball "projectile," are not different enough for us to consider the target to be semi-infinite. Hence, the true impact sliding speed cannot be known in the apparatus of Bowden and Freitag.[18] The situation is further complicated, from our point of view, because unlike metals are involved in most of the tests. Nevertheless, we can make an estimate of the effective sliding velocity, v_f', for fission of the target on the same basis used in hypervelocity-impact experiments.

$$v_f' = v_f m_t / m_p \tag{3.30}$$

where, in this case, v_f is the fission velocity of the target (pad) material ($v_f \cong \sqrt{v_1 \cdot c_s}$), m_t is the mass of the atoms in the target (pads), and m_p is the mass of the atoms in the spinning ball (i.e., Fe atoms).

Values of v_f' for copper and aluminum with a steel ball become 2.16×10^4 and 1.41×10^4 cm/sec, respectively, by this method. Bowden and Freitag[18] note that, above about 1.5×10^4 cm/sec, "a new type of surface damage" is found in these metals. During sliding at high speeds, considerable amounts of copper and aluminum are also transferred to the steel balls; an aluminum alloy (24S) had a rough contact area with numerous metal fragments, up to 2×10^{-2} cm in diameter, found in the vicinity of the contact area. The most spectacular evidence of target fission or break-up is provided by the results with bismuth and antimony pads, as already noted. Here, a shower of metal particles or dust is thrown off above about 2.5×10^4

cm/sec for bismuth, and above 4.0×10^4 cm/sec for antimony. While these are rhombohedral crystals, we may calculate values of limiting slip velocity, v_1, in $<10\bar{1}>$ directions, as for fcc metals:

$$v_1 \text{ (bismuth)} \quad = 0.308 \times 10^3 \text{ cm/sec}$$

$$v_1 \text{ (antimony)} = 0.562 \times 10^3 \text{ cm/sec}$$

Corresponding fission velocities, v_f, are found from a knowledge of the sound velocities[21]; for a steel projectile (spinning ball), we then calculate v_f' from Eq. 3.30.

$$v_f' \text{ (bismuth)} \quad \cong 2.16 \times 10^4 \text{ cm/sec}$$

$$v_f' \text{ (antimony)} \cong 2.30 \times 10^4 \text{ cm/sec}$$

These predicted velocities are somewhat lower than those for which pronounced break-up or powdering of the bismuth and antimony targets is found, but we expect that the *actual* impact velocities will be less than the apparent velocities reported by Bowden and Freitag, because they have not taken into account deformation or motion of the target pads and/or holders at impact. The use of large, massive target pads in this apparatus would enable reliable quantitative determinations of actual sliding speeds at impact. Pads of two or three-inch diameter and several inches thick would have to be substituted for the one-fourth inch diameter pads of one-sixteenth inch thickness to even approach semi-infinite target conditions, however.

In spite of the lack of appropriate data for exact numerical confirmation of the predicted fission effects of high-speed sliding friction, we cannot fail to be gratified that the main features of this phenomenon are found to occur in the velocity range expected.

A third feature of the particle-wave expression for the frictional coefficient is that directional effects are expected in single crystals (or other oriented materials) where the crystal spacing, d, varies in different directions. This is easily seen from Eq. 5.12 below

$$\mu' = \tan \arcsin \left[\frac{\sin\left(\frac{m\boldsymbol{d}}{2\hbar} v\right) \cos\left(\frac{m\boldsymbol{d}}{2\hbar} v\right)}{\left(\frac{m\boldsymbol{d}}{2\hbar} v\right)} \right] \tag{5.12}$$

For a fixed sliding speed, v, the angle $(vm\mathbf{d}/2\hbar)$ will decrease with decreasing $\mathbf{d}$, and this results in a *higher* value of μ'. The changes in μ' with $\mathbf{d}$ will be most pronounced at low values of velocity, where the angle $(vm\mathbf{d}/2\hbar)$ is small, so that the refracted particle wave is near the surface $(\theta_c = 90°)$. In fact, it is evident from Eq. 5.12 that $\mathbf{d}$ and v occupy equivalent positions in the equation, so that, for a fixed velocity, the variation of μ' with $\mathbf{d}$ will resemble the velocity dependence shown in Figures 5.6 and 5.7. Curves of μ' vs. v for three different lattice spacings are shown in Figure 5.16. From Eq. 5.12, therefore, we expect that values of the coefficient of friction in single crystals will be *highest* in the directions of closest spacing, that is, in the slip directions. Now, this expectation *is in direct contradiction* to that following from the welding–plastic deformation explanation, in which we anticipate the *lowest* sliding resistance in close-packed

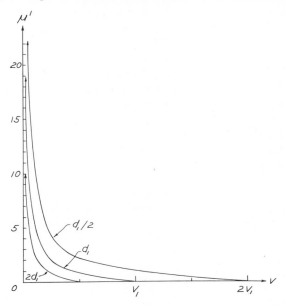

Fig. 5.16. The variation of the coefficient of friction, μ', with velocity, v, according to Eq. 5.12 of the text, for three different lattice spacings: $2\mathbf{d}_1$, $\mathbf{d}_1$, $\mathbf{d}_1/2$. At a given velocity, μ' is greatest for the smallest spacing; the difference is most pronounced at low velocities. As a result, the coefficient of friction for sliding on a single-crystal surface should be highest in directions of closest spacing (slip directions).

directions, where slip occurs most readily. Measurements of sliding friction on various faces of copper single crystals have been made by Bailey[22] and Bailey and Gwathmey,[23] and support the particle-wave view of sliding friction. That is, values of the static coefficient of friction on a particular face are highest in directions of closest spacing on that face. For example, with a hemispherical sapphire slider of 7.94×10^{-2} cm diameter (~ 0.2 in.) sliding on a (100) copper face in air, values of μ were 0.02 in the four $<100>$ directions, but rose to 0.10 in the four $<110>$ directions, a fivefold increase. Smaller-diameter sapphire sliders also indicated largest values of μ in the $<110>$ direction. Similar frictional anisotropies were found for sliding on (110), (111), and (211) faces in air, and on (100), (110), and (111) faces in an hydrogen atmosphere. A polycrystalline copper ball was also used as a slider, and a similar directional dependence found. Some of Bailey's results are summarized in Table 5.1, and a polar plot of μ vs. azimuthal angle for a (100) copper face is shown in Figure 5.17. In connection with these data, we emphasize that the level of values of the frictional coefficient varies greatly for different faces of the crystal, as clearly described by Gwathmey, Leidheiser, and Smith.[24] Hence, the effect of lattice spacing can only be seen from directional sliding experiments on a given crystal face, where all tests are carried out under the same ambient conditions.

Dyer[25] has determined the directional dependence of *rolling* friction on the (100) face of a copper crystal in air. In his experiments, a $\frac{1}{4}$-in. diameter sapphire ball was rolled over the (100) face of a

TABLE 5.1

Directional Variation of Sliding Friction on Single Crystals of Copper[a]

Diameter of sapphire slider 10^{-4} cm	(100) Face Direction		(110) Face Direction	
	Min $<100>$	Max $<110>$	Min $<100>$	Max $<110>$
22	0.23	0.67	0.19	0.50
63	0.12	0.32	0.10	0.28
794	0.02	0.10	0.01	0.08

[a] Measured in air with 25-gram normal load (from data of Bailey[22] and Bailey and Gwathmey[23]).

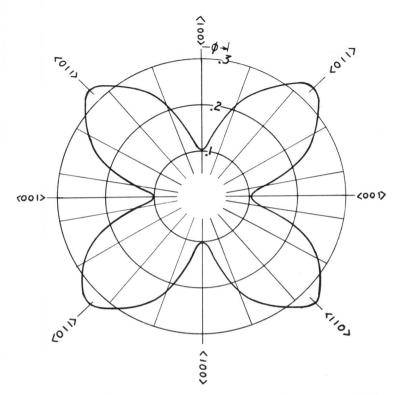

Fig. 5.17. Polar plot of the coefficient of static friction, μ, vs. azimuthal angle, ϕ, for a hemispherical sapphire slider on a (100) face of a copper single crystal. Highest values of μ occur in $<110>$ directions, as expected from Eq. 5.12 and Figure 5.16 (from data of Bailey[22] and Bailey and Gwathmey[23]).

crystal $\frac{1}{2} \times \frac{3}{4} \times 3$ in. Under a normal load of 200 grams, Dyer found a value of 0.897 ± 0.040 for μ in $<100>$ directions, but a value of 1.180 ± 0.013 in $<110>$ directions, in agreement with Bailey's findings for sliding friction.

Directional variations in the coefficient of kinetic friction and the wear of single crystals of sapphire sliding on water-lubricated steel have also been described by Duwell,[26] and a directional dependence of friction, for a hemispherical diamond stylus sliding on a diamond cube face, has been described by Seal,[27] where four peaks in friction are noted, reflecting the fourfold symmetry of a (100) face. The directions of high friction were also those of high (easy) abrasion for the diamond. The frictional anisotropy was found to depend on the orientations of both of the diamonds and the sliding direction; largest values of friction occurred when the direction of sliding and the directions of easy abrasion (high wear) of both diamonds were coincident. Frictional anisotropies of a factor of 3 or more were found on certain surfaces, but a factor of 2 was more usual. The directional dependence of wear and friction in diamond crystals has also been described by Kenyon,[28] by Scott,[29] and by Wentorf.[30]

Most of these investigators have pointed out that the occurrence of high friction in directions of easy abrasion or wear is difficult to explain in terms of the local-welding plus plastic-deformation view of sliding friction. According to this view, the resistance to sliding occurs because of local bonding between the two crystal surfaces at sharp projections and/or plastic deformation between interlocking asperities. The frictional force then should be smallest in directions of easy fracture or plastic flow, where the bonds can be most easily broken or the asperities sheared off. Instead, just the opposite is observed. Ductile materials, such as fcc metals, have *high* coefficients of friction in directions of easy deformation (slip); brittle materials, such as sapphire and diamond, have *high* coefficients of friction in directions of easy fracture (abrasion). The particle-wave expression for the frictional coefficient (Eq. 5.12) predicts high values in close-packed directions (i.e., slip directions), in agreement with the experimental results for copper and sapphire, where slip directions are known. The situation for diamond is not as clear because its lattice structure is more complicated.

In many friction tests, a small hemispherical rider is pressed against the surface of a massive disk revolving at constant angular velocity.[31] The resulting average tangential force on the rider is then obtained by means of strain gages attached to the arm or beam holding the rider; these gages are sensitive to horizontal deflections of the rider beam, and a corresponding stress-deflection calibration allows the determination of the frictional tangential force. Bison, Johnson, and Swikert[31] have determined coefficients of friction for a spherical steel rider ($\frac{1}{8}$-in. diameter) against a steel disk at velocities up to 5.09×10^3 cm/sec (167 ft/sec) in this way. Their results are shown in Figure 5.18, where it is seen that a plateau or region of constant frictional coefficient exists from 0 to 1.27×10^3 cm/sec. These measurements were carried out on unlubricated surfaces in air, however, where it was known that a 25-Å thick film of Fe_3O_4 was present on the steel surfaces. Bowden and Young[32] have measured static coefficients up to 3.5 between steel surfaces previously outgassed at 1000°C. Thus, in looking for experimental data to decide the behavior of μ', we must be careful to select data under conditions where each theoretical equation applies. In order to properly predict the low-velocity sliding behavior of steel on Fe_3O_4, an expression for the group velocity of a particle wave in a diatomic lattice will have to be known; such an expression can be given, but we do not propose to treat such lattices in this first discussion of particle waves in crystals.

The effect of surface contamination on low-velocity values of μ' is most clearly demonstrated by data of Bowden and Persson[19] for steel sliding on clean, flamed glass and on uncleaned glass, as presented in Figure 5.19. At high speeds, the condition of the glass surface is seen

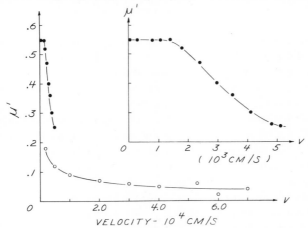

Fig. 5.18. Variation of the coefficient of friction, μ', with velocity for steel sliding against steel, according to Bison et al. (solid points), using a rotating-plate apparatus; and according to Bowden and Persson (open points), from their spinning ball measurements. For similar clean metals measured in a vacuum, a plateau in the μ' vs. v curve as found by Bison (insert) is not expected, but these experiments were carried out in air, and a thin film of Fe_3O_4 was known to be present. Such a film would lower the low-velocity values of friction without effecting the high-velocity values, as discussed in the text (data from references 19 and 32).

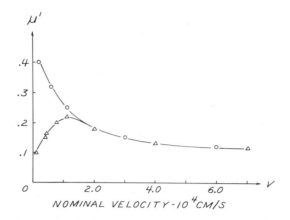

Fig. 5.19. Variation of the coefficient of friction, μ', with velocity for steel against glass, showing the effect of surface contamination at low velocities. Circular points are for clean, flamed glass, while triangular points are for uncleaned glass (from data of Bowden and Persson[19]).

to have no influence on values of the frictional coefficient, as reported also by Freitag.[17] We have anticipated this by noting that the refracted particle wave bends more sharply into the crystal at high velocities, so that the surface structure (as effected by gaseous or liquid impurities) will not be important.

Another feature of the sliding behavior, noted by both Bowden and Freitag[18] and Miller,[20] is that the low-velocity values of μ' depend on the initial sliding velocity at which the spinning steel ball in their apparatus (Figure 5.10) contacts the specimen pads. For example, Miller obtained the results shown in Figure 5.14, for steel sliding on silicon carbide, when the initial contact speed of the ball was about 6×10^4 cm/sec, with low-velocity values of μ' rising sharply as the ball decelerated. If the initial sliding speed was less than 2×10^4 cm/sec, however, the values of μ' remained at about 0.2, i.e., did not rise sharply at lower velocities. A similar result was reported by Bowden and Freitag for steel against copper. In both cases, the investigators noted that, when the spinning ball contacted the specimen, a noticeable transfer of metal occurred above certain critical velocities. For a steel ball sliding against copper, transfer of copper to the ball occurred above 1.0×10^4 cm/sec; for a steel ball sliding against SiC, steel was transferred to the SiC above 2.0×10^4

cm/sec. The bonding of the transferred metal to its new base was found to be quite strong. Hence, it is clear (as pointed out by these investigators) that the low-velocity measurements of μ' were really those of copper against copper and steel against steel for cases of initial high-velocity contact. Indeed, according to Eq. 5.20, with unlike metals, extremely high values of μ' at low velocities are not to be expected because of the $1/r$ factor appearing in this expression, e.g., for copper sliding on steel ($r = 1.14$) the maximum value of μ' expected at $v = 0$ is

$$\mu' \text{ (max)} = \tan \arcsin \left(\frac{1}{1.14}\right)$$

$$\cong 1.84 \qquad \text{(copper against iron)}$$

Similarly, the expected maxima for steel sliding on aluminum is ($r = 2.07$),

$$\mu' \text{ (max)} = \tan \arcsin \left(\frac{1}{2.07}\right)$$

$$\cong 0.55 \qquad \text{(iron against aluminum)}$$

Again, it must be emphasized that only a very thin film of transferred metal is necessary to affect changes in μ' at low velocities, where the refracted particle wave lies near the sliding surface.

For molybdenum, antimony, and bismuth, even smaller zero-velocity values of the frictional coefficient are expected if no metal transfer occurs, because of the large mass ratios of these metals with respect to iron. A compilation of the maximum values of μ' (at zero velocity) expected from Eq. 5.20, for the metals of Figure 5.11 sliding against steel, is given in Table 5.2. Since some metal transfer occurred in the actual sliding tests, the experimental results of Figure 5.11 are not expected to agree numerically with the predicted values. In fact, low-velocity seizure was reported for both aluminum and copper, where a large amount of metal transfer occurred. It is an interesting fact, however, that the *relative order* of the measured low-velocity values of μ' agree roughly with the predicted order from Table 5.2; i.e., copper against steel has the highest value of μ', and bismuth against steel has the lowest coefficient of friction, at low velocities.

TABLE 5.2

Values of the Coefficient of Static Friction[a]

Metal	Atomic wt. M_x	Mass ratio[b] r	Coefficient of static friction μ
Copper	63.5	1.14	1.84
Molybdenum	95.5	1.70	0.73
Aluminum	27.0	2.07	0.55
Antimony	121.8	2.18	0.52
Bismuth	209.0	3.74	0.28

[a] For iron sliding against the metals listed, calculated according to $\mu = \tan$ arcsin $(1/r)$, where r is the atomic mass ratio in each case.

[b] The ratio r is either M_x/M or M/M_x (where M is the atomic weight of iron), as necessary to keep $r > 1$. In the first case, the metal specimen slides against the iron, while in the second case, the iron slides against the metal specimen, as explained in the text.

All of these calculations and the experimental results depicted in Figure 5.2 apply only to clean, outgassed samples, and measurements made in a vacuum, of course.

4. OBLIQUE IMPACT

The ideas on refraction of particle waves at an interface advanced to describe sliding friction can be extended to high-velocity impact at oblique incidence. In our previous discussion of impact in Chapter III, normal incidence was considered, and the formation of hemispherical craters in polycrystalline metals was described for normal impact velocities above a certain fission velocity, v_f. According to the ideas just discussed in connection with sliding friction, a projectile approaching a target at a velocity above v_1 will produce a refracted particle wave in the target which is normal to the target surface no matter what the incident angle may be. That is (cf. Figure 5.4a),

$$\sin \theta = \frac{v_b}{v_a} \sin i \qquad (5.4')$$

but

$$v_b/v_a = 0 \qquad \text{for } v_a \geq v_1$$

hence

$$\theta = 0 \qquad \text{for all values of } i$$

When the incident projectile has a velocity above v_f, cratering will be produced by the normal refracted wave, but, because of the tangential component of projectile velocity, an elongated crater is expected, as depicted in Figure 5.20. If the projectile breaks up (fissions) along with the target, then the *deepest part* of the crater should occur at the first point of contact and have a back side resembling that found in normal incidence, as shown in Figure 5.20. That is, after initial contact, the projectile progressively disintegrates as it moves across the target surface and, therefore, produces a narrowing and progressively shallower crater. Such "wrong way" craters are indeed observed in high-velocity oblique impacts as shown, for example, by the results of Kineke[33] and Gehring[34] reproduced in Figure 5.21.

At very high impact velocities, the projectile may disintegrate so rapidly that very little crater elongation is observed; the exact nature of the results will also depend on the relative fission velocities of the projectile and target for unlike materials.

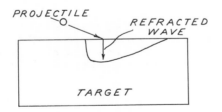

Fig. 5.20. Profile of the expected target crater in a crystal from an obliquely incident projectile, as a result of normal particle-wave refraction at all velocities above $v_1 = h/2md_1$, where d_1 is the closest lattice spacing.

a

b

Fig. 5.21. Replicas of sectioned lead targets showing crater cross sections resulting from impact of an 0.18-gram steel pellet at 5.01 km/sec. (*a*) Impact angle, 62°; (*b*) impact angle, 30° from normal, as shown. In both cases, the crater lip is higher on the side of approach, and the crater wall is steeper than on the opposite side.

Conclusions

There are, naturally, many aspects of sliding friction and lubrication which have not been covered in this brief review of the subject, but we can expect that the particle-wave view will be of general utility in this field. Because of the prevalence of oxide films in most terrestrial sliding experiments, it is really necessary to have a general expression for the group velocity of a particle wave in a diatomic lattice in order to treat properly many of the reported observations of low-velocity and static friction. Particle-wave propagation in diatomic and polyatomic crystals will be considered in the future, but in the meantime, it is gratifying to note that, even within the limitations of a monatomic theory, a number of the experimental facts of sliding friction are properly described. These include:

(*1*) The velocity dependence of the coefficient of friction.

(*2*) The reduction of friction between unlike metals.

(*3*) Directional friction effects in single crystals.

(*4*) The critical dependence of static and slow speed friction on surface properties, and the independence of high-velocity friction with respect to surface conditions.

(*5*) Fracturing and/or powdering of a surface at very high sliding speeds, and metal transfer across sliding surfaces at all speeds.

(*6*) Calculations of coefficients of friction between dry, clean surfaces of unlike metals which are in good agreement with measured values.

The general subject of surface films and lubrication is an area where particle-wave views may also prove useful.

REFERENCES

1. G. Amontons, *Mem. Acad. Sci. Paris, 1699*, 3rd ed., Paris, 1732, pp. 206–227.
2. F. P. Bowden, *Proc. Conf. Lubrication Wear, London, 1957*, The Institution of Mechanical Engineers, London, (1958), pp. 239–245; F. P. Bowden and D. Tabor, *Friction and Lubrication*, Meuthen, London, 1956.
3. A. Gemant, *Frictional Phenomena*, Chemical Publishing Co., Brooklyn, New York, 1950, Chap. XX.
4. G. W. Rowe, *Proc. Conf. Lubrication Wear, London, 1957*, The Institution of Mechanical Engineers, London, (1958) 333–338.
5. F. P. Bowden and T. P. Hughes, *Proc. Roy. Soc. London*, **A172**, 263 (1939); F. P. Bowden and G. W. Rowe, *Proc. Roy. Soc. London*, **A233**, 429 (1956).
6. A. Parent, *Hist. Acad. Sci. Paris*, 1700, 2nd ed., Paris, 1761, pp. 151–152.
7. C. A. Coulomb, *Men. Acad. Roy. Sci.*, Paris, 161 (1785).
8. W. B. Hardy and J. K. Hardy, *Phil. Mag.*, **38**, 32 (1919); *Proc. Roy. Soc. London*, **A112**, 62 (1926); **A118**, 209 (1928).
9. G. A. Thomlinson, *Phil. Mag.*, **7**, 905 (1929).
10. R. Schurnmann, *Engineer*, **168**, 278 (1938); *Proc. Phys. Soc. London*, **52**, 179 (1940); *J. Appl. Phys.*, **11**, 624 (1940).
11. F. P. Bowden and D. Tabor, *The Friction and Lubrication of Solids*, Vol. I, Clarendon Press, Oxford, England, 1950.
12. E. R. Braithwaite, *Solid Lubricants and Surfaces*, Macmillan, New York, 1964.

13. P. B. Hirsch, *Progr. Metal Phys.*, **6**, 236–339 (1956).
14. Equation 5.7 was rendered into the appropriate Latin statement through the kindness of Professor Clifford Truesdell.
15. H. Minshall, *Handbook of Chemistry and Physics*, 41st ed., Chemical Rubber Publishing Co., Cleveland, Ohio, 1959, pp. 2150–2158.
16. C. Galton, *Engineering*, Aug. 23, 1878. Also cited by T. E. Stanton, *Friction*, Longmans, Green, London, 1923, p. 150.
17. E. H. Freitag, *Proc. Conf. Lubrication Wear, London, 1957*; The Institute of Mechanical Engineers, London, (1958) 652–654.
18. F. P. Bowden and E. H. Freitag, *Proc. Roy. Soc. London*, **A248**, 350 (1958).
19. F. P. Bowden and P. A. Persson, *Proc. Roy. Soc. London*, **A260**, 433 (1961).
20. D. R. Miller, *Proc. Roy. Soc. London*, **A269**, 368 (1962).
21. H. B. Huntington, *Solid State Phys.*, **7**, 282 (1958).
22. J. M. Bailey, *Surface Deformation and Friction of Single Crystals of Copper*, Ph.D. Dissertation, University of Virginia, 1959. Univ. Microfilms, Ann Arbor, Mich. Library of Congress Catalog Card No. Mic. 59–4212, 179 pp.
23. J. M. Bailey and A. T. Gwathmey, *Am. Soc. Lubrication Engrs. Trans.*, **5**, 45 (1962).
24. A. T. Gwathmey, H. Leidheiser, and G. P. Smith, *Proc. Roy. Soc. London*, **A212**, 464 (1962); NACA TN No. 1460–61 (1948).
25. L. D. Dyer, *Acta Met.*, **9**, 928 (1961).
26. E. J. Duwell, *J. Appl. Phys.*, **33**, 2691 (1962).
27. M. Seal, *Proc. Conf. Lubrication Wear, London, 1957*, Institution of Mechanical Engineers, London, 1958, p. 252; *Proc. Roy. Soc. London*, **A248**, 379 (1958).
28. D. M. Kenyon, *J. Inst. Petrol.*, **40**, 98 (1954).
29. H. Scott, *Proc. Conf. Lubrication Wear, London, 1957*, Institution of Mechanical Engineers, London, 1958, p. 606.
30. R. F. H. Wentorf, Jr., *J. Appl. Phys.*, **30**, 1765 (1959).
31. E. E. Bison, R. L. Johnson, and M. A. Swikert, *Proc. Conf. Lubrication Wear, London, 1957*, The Institution of Mechanical Engineers, London, 1958, pp. 384–391.
32. F. P. Bowden and J. D. Young, *Proc. Roy. Soc. London*, **A208**, 311 (1951).
33. J. H. Kineke, Jr., *Proc. Fourth Symp. Hypervelocity Impact*, **1**, 10 (1960).
34. J. W. Gehring, Jr., *Proc. Fourth Symp. Hypervelocity Impact*, **2**, 29 (1960).

VI

BROADER IMPLICATIONS

Introduction

In the preceding chapters, some simple ideas on the propagation of particle momentum waves have been applied to various aspects of the mechanical behavior of crystals. The occurrence of non-elastic resonances in vibration experiments, acoustic emission under steady loading, high-velocity impact phenomena, experimental stress–strain curves, and certain features of sliding friction were all successfully described from the particle-wave view. These topics by no means exhaust the usefulness of the particle-wave explanation of deformation and, in this final chapter, a number of additional applications and broader implications will be described.

1. FORMATION OF CRYSTAL MOSAICS

In discussing stress–strain laws in Chapter IV, consideration was given to the generation of additional field-free particles by those initially present. Each original field-free particle was said to be capable of generating another field-free particle after moving a certain distance, x_f, through the applied force field, F, such that

$$Fx_f = u_f \tag{6.1}$$

where u_f is the necessary formation energy for a field-free particle (cf. Figure 6.1). As a rough approximation, u_f was further supposed to be about one-third the dissociation energy, D, since only one vibrational mode (phonon) of three such intrinsic modes was supposedly destroyed by the creation of an interlattice particle. The three modes do not contribute equally to the dissociation energy, however, and therefore the exact value of u_f will depend on which mode is destroyed in the formation process. As a matter of fact, it seems probable that a longitudinal phonon will be destroyed in the act of forming an

177

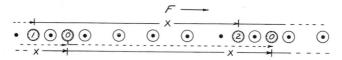

Fig. 6.1. Representation of field-free particles forming additional inter-lattice atoms in a lattice (No's 1, 2, 3 etc.) as the original field-free particles (No. *0*) move a distance $x = F/u_f$ in the applied force field, F, where u_f is the formation energy for an interlattice atom. The vacant lattice sites created simultaneously with the additional field-free particles act as destruction sites for field-free particles. Hence, a linear, instead of an exponential, increase of field-free particles occurs as the force field rises, as explained in the text.

interlattice field-free atom of the type previously described (Chapters I and IV). In this case, u_f will be given by

$$u_f = fmc_t^2/6 = f\frac{D}{6} \cdot \left(\frac{c_\ell}{c_s}\right)^2 \tag{6.2}$$

where c_ℓ is the longitudinal sound velocity, f is an unknown numerical factor less than one, and $D = mc_s^2$. For aluminum, u_f will then be less than or equal to $2D/3$, instead of $D/3$. A list of maximum u_f values calculated in this way for some cubic metals is presented in Table 6.1.

TABLE 6.1

Maximum Values of Formation Energy (u_f) of Interlattice (Field-Free) Particles for Some Cubic Metals.

Metal	Atomic mass 10^{-23} g	Longitudinal sound velocity[a] c_ℓ 10^5 cm/sec	u_f ev/atom[b]
Al	4.48	5.17	$1.28 \cdot f$
Ni	9.74	4.97	$2.50 \cdot f$
Cu	10.55	3.82	$1.60 \cdot f$
Pd	17.66	3.69	$2.51 \cdot f$
Ag	17.89	2.78	$1.44 \cdot f$
Au	32.70	2.06	$1.44 \cdot f$
Pb	34.39	1.43	$0.737 \cdot f$
Th	38.51	2.52	$2.54 \cdot f$

[a] Calculated from the tensile modulus in the slip direction.
[b] $f \leq 1$.

In any case, it is instructive to calculate the necessary generation distance, $x_f = x_1$, corresponding to the limiting force per atom, F_1, for a stationary lattice. That is

$$x_1 = u_f/F_1 \tag{6.1'}$$

but from Chapter IV,

$$F_1 = \frac{1}{2\bar{p}} \frac{m}{d} v_1^2 = \frac{h^2}{8\bar{p}md^3} \qquad \begin{matrix} (6.3) \\ (4.37) \end{matrix}$$

so that

$$x_1 = \frac{u_f 8\bar{p}md^3}{h^2} \tag{6.4}$$

$$= f\frac{4m^2c_i^2 d^3 \bar{p}}{3h^2} \tag{6.4'}$$

and values of x_1 can be calculated for any slip direction with spacing, d_1, in a crystal with atomic masses, m, in terms of the field-free parameter, $\bar{p}$, and the factor, f. Values of x_1 calculated from Eq. 6.4 and experimental values of c_i are given in Table 6.2 for the cubic

TABLE 6.2

Limiting Distances (x_1) between Field-Free Interlattice Atoms Formed
by Mechanical Loading in Cubic Crystals

Metal	Atomic mass 10^{-23} g	u_f ev/atom	Closest lattice spacing d_1 10^{-8} cm	$x_1{}^a$ cm 10^{-3} cm
Al	4.48	$1.28 \cdot f$	2.862	$0.389 \cdot f\bar{p}$
Ni	9.74	$2.50 \cdot f$	2.491	$1.08 \ \cdot f\bar{p}$
Cu	10.55	$1.60 \cdot f$	2.556	$0.819 \cdot f\bar{p}$
Pd	17.66	$2.51 \cdot f$	2.750	$2.67 \ \cdot f\bar{p}$
Ag	17.89	$1.44 \cdot f$	2.880	$1.79 \ \cdot f\bar{p}$
Au	32.70	$1.44 \cdot f$	2.884	$3.28 \ \cdot f\bar{p}$
Pb	34.39	$0.737 \cdot f$	3.499	$3.16 \ \cdot f\bar{p}$
Th	38.51	$2.54 \cdot f$	3.60	$13.2 \ \cdot f\bar{p}$

[a] Both f and $\bar{p}$ are less than one, so that the value given is the maximum limiting distance between interlattice atoms.

metals previously listed in Table 6.1. From Table 6.2 it is clear that the limiting (smallest) distance between field-free particles will be of the order of somewhat less than 10^{-3} cm. This follows since $\bar{p}$ and f, by definition, must each be less than one.

For forces above F_1, the necessary generation distance, x_1', relative to fixed laboratory coordinates, will decrease. However, the lattice moves against each incident free particle for forces above F_1 (cf. Chapter III), so that the *lattice* distance between generated field-free particles will remain equal to x_1. The mean number of field-free particles will continue to increase with force and, thus, a clustering of such particles (atoms) must occur at intervals of x_1 in the lattice. Such accumulations or clusters of field-free particles will, in turn, lead to eventual segmentation of the crystal lattice and the formation of mosaic substructures in crystals with limiting dimensions somewhat less than 10^{-3} cm in most cases. The experimental observations of mosaic structures in crystals, discussed in Chapter II and reviewed by Hirsch,[1] are thus accounted for, and upper limits on the minimum domain sizes are fixed.

In connection with these remarks on field-free particle formation, we recall that in Chapter IV a differential equation describing the force dependence of free-particle formation was given as

$$dQ = Q_0 \frac{F}{u_f} dx$$

(6.5)
(4.53)

where Q_0 represents the number of field-free particles initially present, and dQ is the additional number formed when the original particles move a distance, dx. The motion of field-free particles through a lattice will also result in the *destruction* or disappearance of such particles when vacant lattice sites are encountered. Such vacant sites may exist internally or at the surface of a specimen, but, in particular, we expect numbers of such vacant sites in the vicinity of the field-free particle clusters previously described. The *net* increase in field-free or interlattice atoms will then be given by the *difference* between the additional number formed, dQ_i, and the number destroyed, dQ_v, that is

$$dQ = dQ_i - dQ_v$$

(6.6)

The number of new interlattice atoms formed by motion through a distance, dx, under a force, F, will be

$$dQ_i = Q \frac{F}{u_f} dx \qquad (6.7)$$

Each additional interlattice atom formed, however, will be accompanied by a vacancy, so that the number of *new* vacancies created will be equal to $(Q - Q_0)$, and the consequent additional *destruction* of free-particle atoms for motion through a distance, dx, is given by

$$dQ_v = (Q - Q_0) \frac{F}{u_f} dx \qquad (6.8)$$

As a result, from Eq. 6.6 we obtain Eq. 6.5 used in Chapter IV

$$dQ = Q \frac{F}{u_f} dx - (Q - Q_0) \frac{F}{u_f} dx$$

$$= Q_0 \frac{F}{u_f} dx \qquad (6.5)$$

2. Parabolic Stress–Strain Coefficients

In Chapter IV, it was found that above a certain characteristic resolved stress, $Y_1\Omega_i$, the relation between resolved stress and strain was parabolic

$$(Y_0\Omega_i)^2 = \beta^2 \epsilon_{Li} \qquad \begin{matrix} (6.9) \\ (4.71) \end{matrix}$$

or

$$Y_0\Omega_i = \beta \epsilon_{Li}^{1/2} \qquad (6.9')$$

where the parabolic stress–strain coefficient, β, is given by,

$$\beta = \sqrt{\frac{u_f}{O_i \xi_0 m}} \cdot \frac{\zeta h}{\pi^2 d_1^{5/2}} \qquad (6.10)$$

The symbols used in Eq. 6.10 have their previous meanings, as discussed in Chapter IV; that is, u_f is the formation energy of an interlattice field-free particle; O_i is an orientation factor, which may also depend on the sample shape; ζ represents the number of atoms per cross-sectional area (with normal in the slip direction); d_1 is the lattice spacing in a slip direction; m is the atomic mass; and ξ_0 is the initial number of field-free atoms per unit length in the slip direction. By substituting for u_f in terms of longitudinal sound velocity (Eq. 6.2), the expression for β becomes

$$\beta = \sqrt{\frac{f}{O_i \xi_0 6}} \cdot \frac{c_\ell}{d_1^{5/2}} \cdot \frac{h}{\pi^2} \zeta \qquad (6.11)$$

For a particular type of crystal structure, ζ can be written explicitly in terms of the spacing, d_1; e.g., for fcc crystals

$$\zeta = 1/\sqrt{2}\ d_1^2$$

so that

$$\beta\ (\text{fcc}) = \sqrt{\frac{f}{O_i \xi_0 12}} \cdot \frac{h}{\pi^2} \cdot \frac{c_\ell}{d_1^{9/2}} \qquad (6.11')$$

Hence, for fcc crystals tested under the same initial conditions (same $O_i \xi_0$ values), the parabolic stress–strain coefficients should vary directly as c_ℓ and inversely as the spacing to the nine-halves power. The longitudinal sound velocity must be measured in the slip direction ($<101>$ for fcc crystals); in general, values of c_ℓ may vary considerably for different directions in a crystal,[2] so that comparisons can be made only between c_ℓ values in the slip directions. These can be calculated from a knowledge of Young's modulus, E_{101} in the slip direction, and the density, ρ, according to

$$c_\ell = \sqrt{E_{101}/\rho} \qquad (6.12)$$

Values of E_{101}, in turn, can be obtained from the measured elastic-compliance coefficients, s_{11}, s_{44}, s_{12}, of cubic crystals, as described by Voigt,[3] and others.[4–6] The general expression for E_j in any direction, with direction cosines, α, β, γ, relative to the cube axes, is

$$\frac{1}{E_j} = s_{11} - 2[(s_{11} - s_{12}) - \tfrac{1}{2}s_{44}] \cdot F \qquad (6.13)$$

where $F = \cos^2 \alpha \cos^2 \beta + \cos^2 \beta \cos^2 \gamma + \cos^2 \gamma \cos^2 \alpha$.

Evidently, $F = \frac{1}{4}$ for $<101>$ directions in cubic crystals, so that

$$\frac{1}{E_{101}} = s_{11} - \frac{1}{2}[(s_{11} - s_{12}) - \frac{1}{2}s_{44}] \qquad (6.13')$$

Values of c_t presented in Table 6.1 and used to calculate u_f were found in this way (i.e., by means of Eqs. 6.13 and 6.14). As noted previously, the density of an fcc crystal can always be written in terms of the atomic mass and the spacing, d_1; that is

$$\rho \text{ (fcc) } = \sqrt{2}\, m/d_1^3 \qquad (6.14)$$

As a result, the parabolic coefficient can also be written in terms of the modulus ($E_{101} = E_1$) directly

$$\beta \text{ (fcc) } = \frac{h}{\pi^2}\sqrt{\frac{f}{O_i\xi_0 m\, 12\sqrt{2}}} \cdot \frac{\sqrt{E_1}}{d_1^3} \qquad (6.15)$$

where E_1 is measured in the direction of the spacing, d_1. Equations 6.11 and 6.15 are entirely equivalent, but the latter indicates directly a most remarkable prediction; viz., that the *non-elastic* stress–strain behavior above the characteristic stress, Y_1, is dependent upon the lattice spacing and the *elastic* tensile modulus. Thus, aluminum, gold, and silver, with nearly equal elastic moduli in the $<101>$ directions and almost identical lattice spacings, should have a common parabolic stress–strain coefficient (provided the samples tested have the same $O_i\xi_0 m$ values of course). Parabolic coefficients for nickel, copper, and palladium should be higher than those for aluminum–copper–gold because of higher moduli and smaller spacings, while smaller values for thorium and lead must result from their lower moduli and larger lattice spacings.

The foregoing remarks were predicted on the assumption of common $O_i\xi_0 m$ values for the metals tested, and this is not a completely realistic view, although values of O_i may not vary too much for samples of similar shapes and orientations.

The supposed occurrence of common $\xi_0 m$ values for crystals implies that the formation process creating the initial field-free atoms is such that the number formed is inversely proportional to the mass of the crystal atoms under "normal" or common sample preparation techniques. A common starting point for all metal crystals, for example, might be taken as the liquid state at the melting temperature. Upon solidification, most of the atoms assume relative positions corresponding to the regular lattice structure for each metal, but a certain proportion may assume interlattice positions. Thermodynamic considerations,[7,8] in fact, indicate that, at temperatures above absolute zero, some point defects are required for minimum values of free energy and the most stable configuration or space arrangement of atoms in a solid. The exact number of interlattice atoms present in the solidified material may also depend on the cooling rate; as mentioned before, a sudden chilling or quenching to a low temperature is expected to result in large values of ξ_0, for example. Annealing a solid sample at a temperature a few degrees below melting should result in more or less "standardizing" ξ_0 at a value such that the free energy of the crystal approaches a minimum for the annealing temperature. That is

$$(E - TS) = \min \tag{6.16}$$

where E is the total vibrational (elastic) energy of the lattice per atom, and S is the entropy. As a result of the minimum free-energy condition of Eq. 6.16, the fraction of atoms in interlattice (field-free) sites, n_f, at a temperature, T, can be written as

$$n_f = e^{S_f/k} \cdot e^{-u_f/kT} \tag{6.17}$$

where S_f is the entropy increase resulting from the formation of an interlattice atom, u_f is the formation energy as before, and k is Boltzman's constant. The equilibrium number of interlattice atoms per unit length, ξ_{0e}, can then be obtained by multiplying n_f by the total number of atoms per unit length in the particular direction and lattice under consideration. The *equilibrium* number of field-free atoms per cm could, in principal, be calculated by means of Eq. 6.17 and a knowledge of the values of S_f and u_f, but the *actual* number present, ξ_0, at any temperature would not be known, since there is no certainty that thermodynamic equilibrium has been reached in an actual case. If we suppose that the approach to equilibrium is governed by a self-diffusion process, it is reasonable to expect that, after long times at high annealing temperatures, equilibrium is approached, however. Nothing in these considerations suggests that the product, $\xi_0 m$, should be constant. Indeed, for common values of the ratio, u_f/T, values of ξ_{0e} will be constant; for fcc metals, the ratio of dissociation energy to melting temperature, D/T_M, is about the same in most cases, so that metals annealed near their melting temperatures might be expected to have similar ξ_0 values instead of $\xi_0 m$ values. All of the remarks so far have assumed that the inter-lattice atoms were formed in a completely random fashion in the crystal lattice without regard to direction, but, if the random nature of the formation process is destroyed by the imposition of a biasing force on the atoms, for example, the number of interlattice atoms will be reduced in proportion to the magnitude of the force. Such a biasing force is present in all real crystals as a result of the earth's gravita-tional attraction, mg, and hence the number of field-free interlattice atoms actually formed in a solidified crystal will be reduced in inverse proportion to the atomic mass and

$$\xi_0 m = \text{constant} \tag{6.18}$$

is a reasonable assumption for carefully prepared, annealed, pure single-crystal samples of fcc metals.

In any case, from Eq. 6.15 we cannot obtain absolute values of the parabolic coefficients, since both ξ_0 and f are unknown, but the *ratios* of the coefficients for various metals can be predicted for common $\xi_0 m$ values on the basis of the quantity $\sqrt{E_1}/d_1{}^3$, as given in Table 6.3 for some fcc metals. Aluminum, silver, and gold will have almost identical coefficients, as noted before; the expected ratios between nickel, copper, aluminum–silver–gold, and lead are:

$$\frac{\beta_{Ni}}{\beta_{Cu}} \quad \begin{array}{c} 9.27 \\ \hline 6.97 \end{array} \quad \begin{array}{c} 2.50 \\ \hline 1.86 \end{array}$$

$$\frac{\beta_{Ni}}{\beta_{Cu}}{\beta_{Al,Ag,Au}}{\beta_{Pb}} = \begin{array}{c} 9.27 \\ \hline 6.97 \\ \hline 3.69 \\ \hline 1.12 \end{array} = \begin{array}{c} 2.50 \\ \hline 1.86 \\ \hline 1.00 \\ \hline 0.303 \end{array} \tag{6.19}$$

These particular metals were chosen from Table 6.3 for comparison with the numerous experimental stress–strain data recently compiled

TABLE 6.3

Values of $\sqrt{E_1}/d_1^3$ for Some Cubic Metals Where E_1 and d_1 Are the
Tensile Modulus and Lattice Spacing, Respectively, in the Slip Direction

Metal	Closest lattice spacing d_1 10^{-8} cm	Tensile modulus[a] E_1 10^{11} dynes/cm^2	$\dfrac{\sqrt{E_1}}{d_1^3}$ 10^{28} dynes$^{1/2}$/cm^4
Al	2.862	7.22$_0$	3.65
Ni	2.491	21.9$_7$	9.27
Cu	2.556	13.0$_7$	6.97
Pd	2.750	13.6$_4$	5.68
Ag	2.880	8.09$_0$	3.69
Au	2.884	8.14$_6$	3.71
Pb	3.499	2.32$_8$	1.12
Th	3.60	7.42$_1$	1.83

[a] Calculated from measured elastic-compliance coefficients, as explained in the text.

and analyzed by Bell[9,10] in a review of 200 papers reporting 318 single-crystal tests carried out by 40 investigators over a 40-year period. Some 387 calculations of parabolic coefficients were made by Bell from the original stress–strain data or from derived parameters reported by the investigators. In all cases, it was possible to fit the data beyond some characteristic strain, ϵ_1 (and hence stress, Y_1), by a parabolic resolved stress–resolved strain relation of the form

$$\sigma = (1 - T/T_M)\,\beta_{r0}(\epsilon - \epsilon_1)^{1/2} \qquad (6.20)$$

where T_M is the melting temperature, and T the test temperature, in degrees Kelvin. Values of β_{r0} varied somewhat, as might be expected by us from variations in O_i and ξ_0, but the *average* values of *all* calculated coefficients for each of the metals examined by Bell (cf. Table I, ref. 10) are found to be in the ratio

$$\frac{\beta_{r0}(\text{Ni})}{\beta_{r0}(\text{Cu})} = \frac{\begin{array}{c}15.04\\ \hline 11.82\\ \hline 5.83\\ \hline 1.90\end{array}}{\begin{array}{c}\\ \\ \\ \end{array}} = \frac{\begin{array}{c}2.58\\ \hline 2.03\\ \hline 1.00\\ \hline 0.32\end{array}}{} \qquad (6.21)$$

$$\frac{\beta_{r0}(\text{Ni})}{\beta_{r0}(\text{Cu})} \; \frac{}{\beta_{r0}(\text{Al, Ag, Au})} \; \frac{}{\beta_{r0}(\text{Pb})}$$

$\beta_{r0}(\text{Ni})$	15.04	2.58
$\beta_{r0}(\text{Cu})$	11.82	2.03
$\beta_{r0}(\text{Al, Ag, Au})$	5.83	1.00
$\beta_{r0}(\text{Pb})$	1.90	0.32

(Bell's experimental compilation)

The above results are based on 222 calculated β_{r0} values for aluminum, silver, and gold; 95 calculated β_{r0} values for copper; 41 β_{r0} values for nickel; and 28 β_{r0} values for lead. Not included are 16 tests on copper crystals,[9] with initial orientations near the 111 or 100 corners of the standard stereographic triangle, which give an average value of $\beta_{r0} = 14.3$ kg/mm^2 instead of the 11.82 kg/mm^2 found for central orientations.

The ratios of parabolic coefficients predicted in Eq. 6.19 (2.50/1.86/1.00/0.30) are seen to be in remarkably close agreement with the *averages* of the experimental values calculated by Bell and presented in Eq. 6.21 (2.58/2.03/1.00/0.32). From Eq. 6.15, we expect that individual values of β will vary with the initial orientation factor, Ω_i, since $O_i = \Omega_i S_i / L$. However, values of Ω_i do not vary much for central orientations, as illustrated by the contour lines of equal orientation factors[11] shown in Figure 6.2, so that the widest variations from the average should occur near the corners. In any case, variations in Ω_i are minimized since it appears to the one-half power in the expression for β. Bell's calculations (cf. Table I in ref. 10) do reveal considerable variation from the average value of β_{r0}; in 172 calculations for aluminum with an average β_{r0} of 5.61 kg/mm^2, maximum and minimum values were 13.38 and 1.66 kg/mm^2, respectively, although the majority of the values were much closer to the average. For example, 143 of the aluminum values (83%) were within $\pm 30\%$

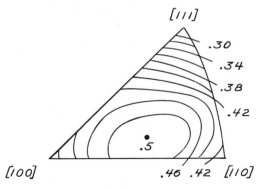

Fig. 6.2. Contour lines of the equal orientation factor, Ω, as a function of specimen-axis orientation, as specified in the standard stereographic triangle. Note that central orientations have nearly the same value of Ω; only near the corners do the values drop considerably from those in the center.

TABLE 6.4

Summary of 385 Parabolic Coefficient (β_{r0}) Calculations by Bell[a] from
Experimental Single-Crystal Stress–Strain Data on Six fcc Metals

Metal	Average value of β_{r0} kg/mm²	No. of calculated values	% Within ± 30% of average	Extreme values kg/mm²	
				Min.	Max.
Pb	1.90	28	75	1.25	3.43
Al	5.61	172	83	1.66	13.38
Au	6.20	26	96	5.04	8.32
Ag	7.05	24	100	5.42	9.08
Al, Ag, Au	5.83	222	82	1.66	13.38
Cu	11.82	94	73	3.09	19.90
Ni	15.04	41	68	9.13	31.11

[a] Bell[10] has subdivided the β_{r0} values for some of the metals into various groups according to an empirical scheme, but there is no reason for such subdivision, according to our development, unless ξ_0 is in some way limited to a few discrete values.

of the average. In 26 calculated values for gold with an average β_{r0} of 6.20 kg/mm², the extremes were 8.32 and 5.04 kg/mm²; 28 lead values averaged to a β_{r0} of 1.90 kg/mm² with extremes of 3.43 and 1.25 kg/mm², etc. A summary of the average experimental parabolic coefficients is presented in Table 6.4.

The temperature dependence of the parabolic coefficients described by Bell also follows from Eq. 6.15, since E_1 will decrease and d_1 will increase with increasing temperature.

The experimental finding of a parabolic stress–strain region for these six metals and the close agreement between predicted and observed ratios of average parabolic coefficients lend strong support to the particle-wave view of deformation.

3. Lattice Momentum Field—A Third Force

We now return to the differential equation for particle momentum waves in a lattice introduced in Chapter I. This was set up as a momentum-transfer equation for a row lattice on the basis of con-

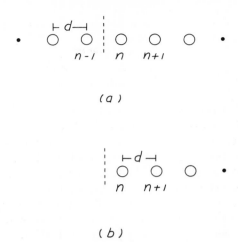

(a)

(b)

Fig. 6.3. (a) Schematic representation of three lattice masses at equilibrium sites ($n - 1$, n, $n + 1$) in a row lattice of spacing, d. Momentum interactions at n may occur between $n - 1$, n, and n, $n + 1$ masses (atoms). (b) Lattice of (a) with atoms to the left of the nth mass removed. Momentum interaction at n now may occur only between n, $n + 1$ masses.

servation of momentum, and gave the net force on the nth atom in a row (Fig. 6.3a),

$$F_n = m \, \frac{\partial v_n}{\partial t} = \frac{i\hbar}{2d^2} \, (v_{n+1} + v_{n-1} - 2v_n) \qquad (6.22)$$

Instead of describing the force in terms of the velocity difference between a general nth atom and its neighbors, we can describe this force in terms of a *lattice momentum field*, $\mathcal{P}$, such that

$$F_n = \mathcal{P} \cdot mv_n \qquad (6.23)$$

where the momentum field, $\mathcal{P}$, now replaces the discrete lattice and specific reactions between other lattice masses and the mass at n. In order for this field description to be equivalent to the previous atomistic view, it is necessary that the force on the nth mass (atom) be the same in each case, and hence from Eqs. 6.22 and 6.23 we obtain

$$\mathcal{P} = \frac{i\hbar}{2md^2} \left(\frac{v_{n+1}}{v_n} + \frac{v_{n-1}}{v_n} - 2 \right) \qquad (6.24)$$

Substitution of the previously determined expressions for v_n, v_{n+1}, and v_{n-1} from Eqs. A.2 to A.4 yields

$$\mathscr{P} = -i\,\frac{2\hbar}{m\boldsymbol{d}^2}\,\sin^2\left(\frac{k\boldsymbol{d}}{2}\right) \tag{6.25}$$

where $k = 2\pi/\lambda$ is now the wave vector (and λ, the wavelength) associated with the lattice momentum field. The value of k (and hence $\mathscr{P}$) will depend on a free-particle velocity, v_i, through the de Broglie relation, if the field description of lattice behavior is to be equivalent to the previous development. That is, the momentum field of a lattice will depend on the velocity of an external or internal initially-free particle which, in effect, generates the lattice field since $k = mv_i/\hbar$. This dependence of the momentum field on free-particle velocity is similar to the generation of a magnetic field, $\mathbf{B}$, by a moving charge. A second charge q moving with velocity v in the magnetic field is acted on by a Force, $\mathbf{F} = q\mathbf{v} \times \mathbf{B}$ in close analogy with the situation represented by Eq. 6.23, for example.

The one-dimensional differential equation given by Eq. 6.22 applies directly to any direction $\boldsymbol{d}_j$ in a three-dimensional crystal according to Section 6 of Chapter I and Appendix B. Hence, an expression for the magnitude of the momentum field for a particular direction in a three-dimensional lattice can be written from Eq. 6.25

$$\mathscr{P}_j = \frac{2\hbar}{m\boldsymbol{d}_j^2}\,\sin^2\left(\frac{k_j \boldsymbol{d}_j}{2}\right) \tag{6.26}$$

where k_j represents the component of wave vector in the direction with lattice spacing $\boldsymbol{d}_j$.

From Eq. 6.26 we readily realize that the magnitude of the lattice momentum field will be a maximum, for a fixed value of $\boldsymbol{d}_j$, whenever

$$\frac{k_j \boldsymbol{d}_j}{2} = q\,\frac{\pi}{2}$$

or

$$q\lambda = 2\boldsymbol{d}_j \sin\theta \tag{6.27}$$

where

$$k_j = \frac{mv_i \sin\theta}{\hbar}$$

and where θ is the angle between the free-particle velocity and the crystal surface perpendicular to d_j, and $q = 1, 2, 3, 4 \ldots$

There will also be certain values of λ for which the momentum field is zero, corresponding to $k_j d_j / 2 = q\pi$. These conditions for maximum and zero values of momentum field correspond closely to the space grating relation (Bragg diffraction equation) for waves in a crystal (cf. Eq. 1.5 of Chapter I).

We also note from Eq. 6.26 that the maximum values of $\mathcal{P}$, which occur when Eq. 6.27 is satisfied will be large for directions in a crystal where d_j is small. These ideas on lattice momentum fields can be used to fashion an improved explanation of the diffraction of particles by crystals, but this explanation will be developed at length elsewhere.

The form of the expression for lattice momentum field suggests that any periodically spaced group of two or more particles might have an associated momentum field with magnitude

$$\mathcal{P}_0 \cong \frac{\hbar}{mr^2} \tag{6.28}$$

for particles of mass m and spacing, r. Similarly a particle of mass m' and velocity v' approaching particles of mass m might be expected to experience a force of amplitude, F_0, where

$$F_0 = \frac{\hbar}{mr^2} m'v' \tag{6.29}$$

Such a force would be short-range and strong for small values of m relative to m', in contrast to gravitational forces between masses which depend on the product mm'. At "contact" distances of the order of 3×10^{-8} cm, and a velocity of 5×10^5 cm/sec, this force will be about 4×10^{-6} dyne/atom for like atoms $(m = m')$. This is of the order of one-hundredth the electrostatic (Coulomb) force between electrons at the same distance, and thus represents a large force. The corresponding stress for aluminum is about 50×10^8 dyne/cm^2.

The existence of such a third force (force de frappé) in high-velocity impact tests might result in interaction between a projectile and target (in vacuum) before "contact" (i.e., before the separation approaches interatomic distances). The effect would be expected to show up in extremely high-velocity impact between a heavy-atom projectile and a light-atom semi-infinite target.

For smaller (subatomic) particles or shorter distances such as those that exist *within* an atom, the momentum field associated with this type of force would be extremely strong, of course.

4. Particle-Wave Oscillators

The remarks in the preceding section are highly speculative, and hence, by way of balance, an extremely practical aspect of particle waves is next considered. This concerns the construction of particle-wave oscillators in which the mechanical energy of unidirectional deformation may be converted into oscillatory energy at audio frequencies. If the plastic deformation of a crystal takes place as a wave process, as outlined in the previous chapters, then the deformation rate or velocity is expected to depend in some manner on the group velocity of the individual particle waves associated with each atom contributing to the deformation. The group velocity of such a particle wave in a crystal lattice is given by

$$v_g = \frac{h}{\pi m \boldsymbol{d}} \sin \frac{k\boldsymbol{d}}{2} \cos \frac{k\boldsymbol{d}}{2} \qquad \begin{matrix}(6.30)\\(1.35)\end{matrix}$$

as already described in Chapter I. The relation between force per atom, F, and wave vector, k, derived in Chapters I and IV, makes possible an expression of particle-wave group velocity in terms of force, as demonstrated below:

$$v_g = \frac{h}{\pi m \boldsymbol{d}} \sin b\sqrt{F} \cos b\sqrt{F} \qquad (6.31)$$

where

$$k = \sqrt{F}/\alpha \qquad b = \boldsymbol{d}/2\alpha = \frac{\boldsymbol{d}}{\hbar}\sqrt{\frac{pm\boldsymbol{d}}{2}} \qquad (6.32)$$

and all symbols have their previous meanings. If a plot of F vs. v_g is now made, as presented in Figure 6.4, we notice that there is a region or range of values of F where the F vs. v_g slope is negative, that is, a

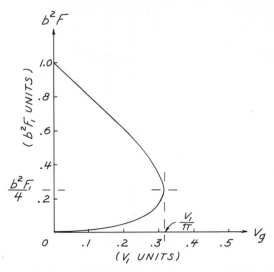

Fig. 6.4. Force per atom (b^2F units) vs. group velocity. (v_g) of a particle-momentum wave in a lattice of spacing, d. Maximum value of v_g is $h/2\pi md$ (or v_1/π) and occurs at $b^2F_1/4$, as shown. Above this value of force, the group velocity decreases so that a region of negative differential mechanical resistance exists.

region of negative differential mechanical resistance. This suggests that a mechanical negative-resistance oscillator can be devised if a suitable arrangement of mass, spring, and negative-resistance crystal element is made to form an equivalent mechanical circuit like that of Figure 6.5a. This circuit is one in which sustained oscillations will occur in the parallel branch AB if ρ_m is a negative differential-resistance device. A mechanical arrangement for the equivalent circuit of Figure 6.5a is shown schematically in Figure 6.5b. The conditions for sustained velocity oscillations (and hence, oscillating displacements) in the circuit of Figure 6.5a are easily found from standard circuit analysis to be:

$$\rho_m = \frac{\partial F}{\partial v_g} \le \frac{-MS_m}{R_m} \tag{6.33}$$

where M is the mass shown in Figure 6.5b, S_m is the elastance of the spring, and R_m is a mechanical resistance arising from air friction

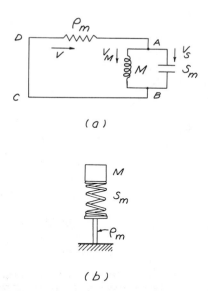

(a)

(b)

Fig. 6.5. (a) Equivalent mechanical circuit diagram of a negative-resistance mechanical oscillator in which ρ_m represents a negative-resistance device (loaded crystal); M and S_m are mass and spring elements, respectively; and v, v_M, and v_S are the velocities of the respective branches of the circuit, as indicated. (b) Schematic representation of a mechanical model for the circuit of (a). If the load on the crystal element, ρ_m, is such that a negative slope exists for the F vs. v_g curve of the crystal, as in Figure 6.4, then sustained oscillations of the external spring–mass combination (S_m, M) may occur as the crystal deforms.

and/or internal friction or damping in the spring. The frequency of oscillation, ν_0, is given by

$$2\pi\nu_0 = \sqrt{\left(\frac{R_m + \rho_m}{M\rho_m}\right) S_m - \frac{1}{4}\left(\frac{R_m}{M} + \frac{S_m}{\rho_m}\right)^2} \qquad (6.34)$$

$$\cong \sqrt{\frac{S_m}{M}} \qquad (6.35)$$

for

$$R_m << \rho_m \qquad \text{and} \qquad \rho_m = -MS_m/R_m$$

Various practical arrangements for obtaining mechanical structures equivalent to the circuit of Figure 6.5a can be devised.[11] In these arrangements, the mass, M, and spring elastance, S_m, can be varied within certain limits to obtain different frequencies, according to Eq. 6.35, provided that the product MS_m is kept within a range that satisfies the negative differential-resistance conditions of Eq. 6.33. The static extension or compression of the spring must likewise be maintained at a value which will produce a load on the crystal element such that the region of negative resistance in the atomic F vs. v_g curve is in operation.

In order to obtain electrical oscillations, a coil may be attached to M and arranged so that it oscillates transversely to magnetic flux lines in an annular gap, or a piezoelectric bilaminate strip may be used as the spring element. In this latter case, no magnet is needed; the elastance of the bilaminate strip provides the spring elastance, S_m, and, at the same time, periodic flexing of the strip produces an oscillating emf across the faces of the laminates.

The audio-frequency resonances described in Chapter II may also be used to construct a particle-wave *feedback* oscillator. That is, the amplitude of vibrations applied to one part or side of a crystal are found to be enhanced at another part or side provided the crystal is under load. Amplification of the vibrations requires an input of energy, which again must be supplied by the unidirectional deformation of the loaded crystal. In order to convert such an amplifier into an oscillator, it is only necessary to provide for feedback of some part of the amplified output vibrations into the input side of the crystal (with proper phase relations).[11]

In both types of oscillators, it is apparent that the loaded crystal acts as a "mechanical" battery which is "charged" by the application of steady loads, and that a substantial amount of energy can be obtained only through considerable deformation.

Final Remarks

Starting with the idea that wave mechanics should be applicable to mechanical properties of solids, a connection between particle waves and deformation has been developed. The connection is such that Planck's constant, h, plays a prominent part, as anticipated. According to the view presented, non-elastic deformation in crystals results from the propagation of internally generated particle momentum waves with the de Broglie wavelength, $\lambda = h/mv_i$. The particle waves in question are not the probability waves of contemporary, orthodox quantum mechanics, but are, instead, real-property waves governed by a differential equation of the form

$$m \frac{\partial v_n}{\partial t} = \frac{i\hbar}{2d^2} \left(v_{n+1} + v_{n-1} - 2v_n \right) \tag{6.36}$$

where v_n is the velocity of a general nth mass (atom) as a result of a particle wave propagating in a lattice with atom masses, m, in a direction with spacing, d. Solutions to this equation for both infinite and finite lattices lead to frequency–wave vector conditions from which a number of interesting results follow. These include the occurrence of characteristic frequencies or modes associated with nonelastic deformation, and the existence of certain critical or limiting velocities of deformation. From these basic ideas, it is possible to form relatively simple, and yet quantitative, explanations of the experimental observations of non-elastic audio-frequency resonances, hypervelocity impact phenomena, stress–strain relations for cubic crystals, sliding friction, and the formation of crystal mosaics. Deformation frequencies, velocities, and even frictional coefficients can be calculated directly in terms of Planck's constant, atomic mass, crystal spacing, and measured quantities like sound velocity. The agreement, in all cases where experimental values are available, ranges from good to excellent. When it comes to stress–strain relations, on the other hand, there are certain defect quantities, the field-free distance parameter, p, and the initial number of field-free atoms per unit length, ξ_0, which are not known exactly. In spite of this, it is possible to obtain the correct form of the stress–strain law and its variation with crystal orientation, temperature, purity, size, and various kinds of sample pretest treatments. Furthermore, the *ratios* of the coefficients of the parabolic part of the stress–strain curve are correctly predicted for six fcc metals. An interesting feature of the stress–strain results is that beyond a certain characteristic stress, Y_1, the resolved stress–resolved strain relation is parabolic,

$$Y_r = \beta \epsilon_r^{1/2} \tag{6.37}$$

and

$$\beta \sim \frac{h}{\sqrt{O_i \xi_0 m}} \frac{\sqrt{E_1}}{d_1^3} \tag{6.38}$$

That is, the non-elastic parabolic coefficient depends jointly on Planck's constant, h, and the tensile elastic modulus, E_1 (measured in the resolved-slip direction), as well as the crystal spacing, d_1. Elastic constants, therefore, do play a part in determining non-elastic deformation; the fission velocity, v_f, discussed in Chapter III, also depends in part on a mean elastic sound velocity, c_s.

The idea that there are real-property waves (momentum waves) associated with moving particles, in addition to the nonphysical probability waves of orthodox quantum theory, is sustained by the success in dealing with mechanical properties which follows from this view. The concept of an alternate real particle wave has also been advanced by de Broglie[12] in his "Theory of the Double Solution," which, however, supposes that the Schroedinger equation is the governing relation for the real waves as well as the usual probability waves. In our case, we have not supposed that both types of waves are solutions of the *same* differential equation; instead a new differential equation has been set up for real-property waves, as given in Eq. 6.36 and described in Chapter I. This new equation has the advantage that simple and comprehensible exact solutions are possible for three-dimensional crystals containing large numbers of atoms. An improved explanation of particle diffraction by crystals also results from these new concepts.

While a number of mechanical phenomena have been successfully described in terms of particle waves, it is obvious that much remains to be discussed. Fracture and creep are yet to be treated, as are diatomic (or polyatomic) lattices and alloys. Some of these topics will be taken up subsequently but, in the meantime, it must already be clear that mechanical properties are not necessarily "all awry"—that the Hand of the Potter did *not* shake!

REFERENCES

1. P. B. Hirsch, in *Progress in Metal Physics, Vol. 6*, B. Chalmers and R. King, eds., Pergamon, New York, 1956, pp. 236–239.
2. E. Schmid and W. Boas, *Plasticity of Crystals*, Hughs, London, 1950.
3. W. Voigt, *Lehrb. d. Kristallphys.*, **739**, 740 (1928).
4. E. Goens, *Ann. Physik*, **38**, 456–468 (1940).
5. H. Rohl, *Ann. Physik*, **16**, 887–906 (1933).
6. E. Goens and J. Weerts, *Physik Z.*, **37**, 321–326 (1936).
7. J. Frenkel, *Kinetic Theory of Liquids*, Oxford University Press, New York, 1946.

8. W. Schottky, *Z. Physik. Chem.*, **B29**, 353–360 (1935).
9. J. F. Bell, *Phil. Mag.*, **10**, 107–126 (1964).
10. J. F. Bell, *Phil. Mag.*, **11**, 1135–1156 (1965).
11. E. R. Fitzgerald, U.S. Patent Application No. 453,439 (1965).
12. L. de Broglie, *The Current Interpretation of Wave Mechanics, A Critical Study*, Elsevier, Amsterdam, 1964.

APPENDIX A

SOLUTION TO THE MOMENTUM-TRANSFER EQUATION IN A ONE-DIMENSIONAL LATTICE

The differential equation for momentum transfer between nearest neighbors in a row lattice with spacing, d, was given in Chapter I in terms of a general nth lattice-point mass and is rewritten below:

$$m \frac{\partial v_n}{\partial t} = \mathbf{K}_p(v_{n+1} + v_{n-1} - 2v_n) \qquad \begin{matrix} (A.1) \\ (1.22) \end{matrix}$$

where $\mathbf{K}_p$ is the momentum transfer constant for the lattice, m is the mass of each lattice atom, and the physical basis for the equation is the principle of conservation of momentum, as discussed in Chapter I.

For an infinitely long lattice, the following running-wave solution is tentatively assumed:

$$v_n(t) = Be^{-i(2\pi\nu t - kn\mathbf{d})} \qquad (A.2)$$

where $k = 2\pi/\lambda$ is the wave vector.

Therefore, it follows that

$$\begin{aligned} v_{n+1}(t) &= Be^{-i[2\pi\nu t - k(n+1)\mathbf{d}]} \\ &= Be^{-i(2\pi\nu t - kn\mathbf{d})} \cdot e^{ik\mathbf{d}} \end{aligned} \qquad (A.3)$$

$$\begin{aligned} v_{n-1}(t) &= Be^{-i[2\pi\nu t - k(n-1)\mathbf{d}]} \\ &= Be^{-i(2\pi\nu t - kn\mathbf{d})} \cdot e^{-ik\mathbf{d}} \end{aligned} \qquad (A.4)$$

and

$$\frac{\partial v_n}{\partial t} = -i2\pi\nu \, Be^{-i(2\pi\nu t - kn\mathbf{d})} \qquad (A.5)$$

Substituting Eqs. A.2–A.5 into Eq. A.1, we get:

$$-i2\pi m\nu = \mathbf{K}_p(e^{ik\mathbf{d}} + e^{-ik\mathbf{d}} - 2) \qquad (A.6)$$

since the expression $Be^{-i(2\pi\nu t - kn\mathbf{d})}$ is common to all terms.

199

Rearranging Eq. A.6, and dividing by 2, yields

$$i\pi m\nu = \mathbf{K}_p \left[1 - \frac{e^{ikd} + e^{-ikd}}{2} \right] \tag{A.7}$$

but,

$$\cos kd = (e^{ikd} + e^{-ikd})/2$$

so that Eq. A.7 can be rewritten as

$$\nu = \frac{-i\mathbf{K}_p}{\pi m} [1 - \cos kd] \tag{A.8}$$

or

$$\nu = \frac{-2i\mathbf{K}_p}{\pi m} \left[\frac{1 - \cos kd}{2} \right] \tag{A.8'}$$

But $(1 - \cos kd)/2 = \sin^2(kd/2)$ and, therefore, the assumed solution is correct provided that the frequency ν is given by

$$\nu = \nu_p = \frac{-2i\mathbf{K}_p}{\pi m} \sin^2 \left(\frac{kd}{2} \right) \tag{A.9}$$

In order for the frequency, ν_p, to be real and positive, the momentum transfer constant, $\mathbf{K}_p$, must be imaginary such that

$$\mathbf{K}_p = iK_p \tag{A.10}$$

whereupon the frequency condition is

$$\nu_p = \frac{2K_p}{\pi m} \sin^2 \left(\frac{kd}{2} \right) \tag{A.11}$$

as given in Chapter I.

For a finite lattice segment of length $S = Nd$, a standing-wave solution to Eq. A.1 is assumed, as mentioned in Chapter II,

$$\nu_n(t) = (B_1 e^{-knd} + B_2 e^{-iknd}) e^{-i2\pi\nu t} \tag{A.12}$$
$$\tag{2.3}$$

Hence,

$$\nu_{n+1}(t) = (B_1 e^{iknd} \cdot e^{ikd} + B_2 e^{-iknd} \cdot e^{-ikd}) e^{-i2\pi\nu t} \tag{A.13}$$

$$v_{n-1}(t) = (B_1 e^{iknd} \cdot e^{-ikd} + B_2 e^{-iknd} \cdot e^{ikd}) e^{-i2\pi\nu t} \qquad (A.14)$$

$$\frac{\partial v_n}{\partial t} = -i2\pi\nu \, [v_n(t)] \qquad (A.15)$$

Substitution of Eqs. A.12–A.15 into Eq. A.1 again yields the frequency condition of Eq. A.6 and, hence, that of Eq. A.11. Now, however, the boundary conditions on the ends of the segment that

$$v_0(t) = v_N(t) = 0 \qquad \text{for all } t$$

require in addition that $B_1 = -B_2$ and that values of wave vector, k, be discrete, as already shown in Chapter II (cf. Eq. 2.5).

APPENDIX B

MOMENTUM TRANSFER IN TWO- AND THREE-DIMENSIONAL LATTICES

In discussing particle-wave propagation in a one-dimensional lattice, a parallel consideration and comparison with elastic waves was carried out. This same procedure can be followed for two- and three-dimensional lattices, but here a major difference, not present in the one-dimensional case, is immediately apparent. That is, there is a difference in coupling between wave components for the two kinds of waves. This difference is present in both two-dimensional and three-dimensional lattices and, since it is somewhat easier to describe in two dimensions, will be shown first for this case.

Consider, then, a two-dimensional or square lattice, as shown in Figure B.1, and a general point (n,r) in the lattice. Such a point will have four "nearest" neighbors at a distance, d, and four "next-nearest" neighbors at a distance, $\sqrt{2}d$. We consider central elastic interactions between the point (n,r) and its nearest neighbors at $(n-1,r)$, $(n,r+1)$, $(n+1,r)$, $(n,r-1)$ to be described by an elastic-interaction constant, K_e, and the corresponding forces or interactions between (n,r) and the next-nearest neighbors at $(n-1,r+1)$, $(n+1,r+1)$, $(n+1,r-1)$, $(n-1,r-1)$ by an elastic constant, L_e. Interactions between n,r and other atoms in the lattice are ignored in this approximation. Then, if $x_{n,r}$, $x_{n+1,r}$, etc., and $y_{n,r}$, $y_{n+1,r}$, etc., represent small displacements of the (n,r), $(n+1,r)$, etc. points from their equilibrium positions in the x and y directions, the differential equations for the motion of the n,r point are:

$$m\frac{\partial^2 x_{n,r}}{\partial t^2} = -[K_e(x_{n,r} - x_{n-1,r})] - [K_e(x_{n,r} - x_{n+1,r})]$$

$$- [(L_e/2)(x_{n,r} - x_{n-1,r+1})] - [(L_e/2)(x_{n,r} - x_{n+1,r+1})]$$

$$- [(L_e/2)(x_{n,r} - x_{n+1,r-1})] - [(L_e/2)(x_{n,r} - x_{n-1,r-1})]$$

$$+ [(L_e/2)(y_{n,r} - y_{n-1,r+1})] - [(L_e/2)(y_{n,r} - y_{n+1,r+1})]$$

$$- [(L_e/2)(y_{n,r} - y_{n-1,r-1})] + [(L_e/2)(y_{n,r} - y_{n+1,r-1})]$$

$$(B.1)$$

$$m \frac{\partial^2 y_{n,r}}{\partial t^2} = - [K_e(y_{n,r} - y_{n,r-1})] - [K_e(y_{n,r} - y_{n,r+1})]$$

$$- [(L_e/2)(y_{n,r} - y_{n+1,r-1})] - [(L_e/2)(y_{n,r} - y_{n+1,r+1})]$$

$$- [(L_e/2)(y_{n,r} - y_{n-1,r+1})] - [(L_e/2)(y_{n,r} - y_{n-1,r-1})]$$

$$+ [(L_e/2)(x_{n,r} - x_{n+1,r-1})] - [(L_e/2)(x_{n,r} - x_{n+1,r+1})]$$

$$- [(L_e/2)(x_{n,r} - x_{n-1,r-1})] + [(L_e/2)(x_{n,r} - x_{n-1,r+1})]$$

(B.2)

The above equations can be simplified, but are written out first term-by-term for purposes of identification with the numbered nearest-neighbor masses $(1,3,5,7)$ and next-nearest-neighbor masses $(2,4,6,8)$ of the square lattice of Figure B.1. Thus, the first bracketed term of Eq. B.1 represents the contribution to the x component of force resulting from a net displacement in the x direction between n,r and No. 1; the second term, from No. 5; the third term, from No. 2; the fourth term, from No. 4; the fifth term, from No. 6; and the sixth term, from No. 8. Then follow four terms which represent

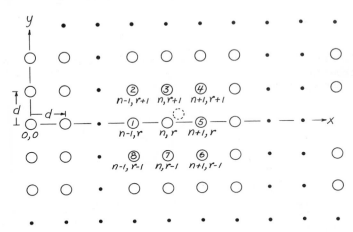

Fig. B.1. Schematic representation of a two-dimensional square lattice of equal point masses with spacing, **d**. Solid circles represent equilibrium positions of masses, the dashed circle represents a possible position of the point (n,r) displaced from equilibrium.

contributions to the x component of force resulting from net displacements in the y direction between n,r and No. 2 (seventh term); No. 4 (eighth term), No. 8 (ninth term), and No. 6 (tenth term). Neither x nor y small displacements of nearest-neighbor masses 3 and 7 contribute to an x component of force, as will be shown.

The y components of force enumerated in Eq. B.2 are similar in origin to those of Eq. B.1, except that now the first two terms arise from net y displacements between n,r and nearest neighbors 7 and 3. The last four terms represent contributions to the y component of force on n,r arising from x components of displacement, and there is no contribution from the small displacements of numbers 1 and 5.

The exact manner in which x and y displacements of the next-nearest neighbors produce x components of force on the mass at n,r can best be seen with the aid of Figures B.2 and B.3, respectively. In

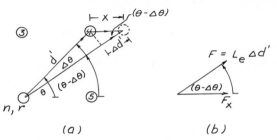

Fig. B.2. Diagram showing how a small x displacement of next-nearest neighbor (a) produces an x component of force, F_x, on the general point (n,r) in a square lattice (b).

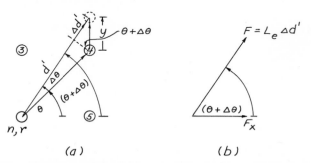

Fig. B.3. Diagram showing how a small y displacement of next-nearest neighbor (a) produces an x component of force, F_x, on the general point (n,r) in a square lattice (b).

Figure B.2, we see that a displacement, x, of the next-nearest neighbor (No. 4) increases the distance, d', between point n,r and No. 4 by an amount, $\Delta d'$. This, in turn, produces a force on n,r given by

$$F = L_e \Delta d' \tag{B.3}$$

in the direction of the new vector distance

$$\mathbf{d''} = \mathbf{d'} + \mathbf{x}$$

where L_e is the elastic-interaction constant between point n,r and its nearest neighbors. The x component of the force is

$$F_x = F \cos (\theta - \Delta\theta) \cong F \cos \theta$$

for small values of x and $\Delta\theta$. Also, we see from Figure B.2 that

$$\Delta d' = x \cos (\theta - \Delta\theta) \cong x \cos \theta$$

so that

$$F_x = L_e x \cos^2 \theta \tag{B.4}$$

for small values of x. For a square lattice, $\theta = 45°$ for next-nearest neighbors and $\cos^2 \theta = \frac{1}{2}$, whence

$$F_x = (L_e/2) \, x \tag{B.5}$$

We note that a small x displacement of nearest-neighbor No. 3 produces no x component of force, since $\theta = 90°$ and $\cos^2 \theta = 0$ for this case, in agreement with our previous remarks.

Next, consider Figure B.3 in which a displacement, y, of the next-nearest neighbor again increases the distance, d', by an amount, $\Delta d'$, producing a force, as given in Eq. B.3. The x component of this force is, however

$$F_x = F \cos (\theta + \Delta\theta) \cong F \cos \theta$$

for small values of y and $\Delta\theta$. Further, we now have

$$\Delta d' = y \sin (\theta + \Delta\theta) \cong y \sin \theta$$

so that

$$F_x = L_e y \cos \theta \sin \theta \tag{B.6}$$

for small values of y. Since $\theta = 45°$, we again have

$$F_x = (L_e/2)y \tag{B.7}$$

A small y displacement of nearest-neighbor No. 5 produces no x component of force, since $\theta = 0°$ and $\sin \theta = 0$ for this case.

The important result of these calculations is that the x and y components of an elastic-displacement wave in a two-dimensional lattice are interdependent or coupled; that is, the differential equation for displacement in the x direction has terms in y, and vice versa. Hence, two simultaneous second-degree differential equations must be solved in order to obtain the variations of frequency with wave vector or other characteristics of the wave motion. Equations B.1 and B.2 can first be simplified, yielding

$$m\frac{\partial^2 x_{n,r}}{\partial t^2} = -K_e(2x_{n,r} - x_{n-1,r} - x_{n+1,r})$$
$$- (L_e/2)(4x_{n,r} - x_{n-1,r+1} - x_{n+1,r+1} - x_{n+1,r-1}$$
$$- x_{n-1,r-1}) + (L_e/2)(y_{n+1,r+1} - y_{n-1,r+1} + y_{n-1,r-1}$$
$$- y_{n+1,r-1}) \tag{B.1'}$$

$$m\frac{\partial^2 y_{n,r}}{\partial t^2} = -K_e(2y_{n,r} - y_{n,r-1} - y_{n,r+1})$$
$$- (L_e/2)(4y_{n,r} - y_{n+1,r-1} - y_{n+1,r+1} - y_{n-1,r+1}$$
$$- y_{n-1,r-1}) + (L_e/2)(x_{n+1,r+1} - x_{n+1,r-1} + x_{n-1,r-1}$$
$$- x_{n-1,r+1}) \tag{B.2'}$$

Possible solutions for the x and y displacements of point n,r then are:

$$x_{n,r} = Ae^{-i(2\pi\nu t - k_1 nd - k_2 rd)} \tag{B.8}$$

$$y_{n,r} = Be^{-i(2\pi\nu t - k_1 nd - k_2 rd)} \tag{B.9}$$

where the two-dimensional wave vector, k, has components k_1 and k_2, respectively. Equations B.8 and B.9 can be differentiated and substituted into Eqs. B.1' and B.2', using appropriate values of n and r to give two linear simultaneous equations in the constants A and B. These are

$$A\left[K_e(1 - \cos k_1\boldsymbol{d}) + L_e(1 - \cos k_1\boldsymbol{d} \cos k_2\boldsymbol{d}) - 2\pi^2\nu^2 m\right]$$
$$+ B\left[L_e \sin k_1\boldsymbol{d} \sin k_2\boldsymbol{d}\right] = 0 \qquad \text{(B.10)}$$

and

$$A\left[L_e \sin k_1\boldsymbol{d} \sin k_2\boldsymbol{d}\right] + B\left[K_e(1 - \cos k_2\boldsymbol{d}) + L_e(1\right.$$
$$\left. - \cos k_1\boldsymbol{d} \cos k_2\boldsymbol{d}) - 2\pi^2\nu^2 m\right] = 0 \qquad \text{(B.11)}$$

Equations B.10 and B.11 may be solved for A and B, but in order for a nonzero solution to exist, it is necessary that the determinant of the coefficients of A and B also be equal to zero; this condition leads to a quadratic equation in ν^2 as a function of k_1 and k_2. That is, let

$$L_e \sin k_1\boldsymbol{d} \sin k_2\boldsymbol{d} = g(k_1, k_2)$$

$$L_e(1 - \cos k_1\boldsymbol{d} \cos k_2\boldsymbol{d}) = f(k_1, k_2)$$

then

$$\begin{vmatrix} K_e(1 - \cos k_1\boldsymbol{d}) + f(k_1, k_2) - 2\pi^2\nu^2 m & g(k_1, k_2) \\ g(k_1, k_2) & K_e(1 - \cos k_2\boldsymbol{d}) + f(k_1, k_2) - 2\pi^2\nu^2 m \end{vmatrix} = 0$$

$$\text{(B.12)}$$

Hence, in general, for any given direction (specified by a pair of k_1, k_2 values) in the square lattice of Figure B.1, there will be *two* ν vs. k curves which can be constructed only if values of both K_e and L_e are known. A representation of the general dependence of ν vs. k for all directions can be constructed in the form of three-dimensional surfaces, with k_1 and k_2 as coordinates in a plane and the height above the $k_1 k_2$ plane to the surface set equal to ν. For particular combinations of k_1, k_2 (direction in k space), the two equations giving ν vs. k are easily obtained. For example, if we consider a [10] direction, then

$$k_2 = 0 \qquad \sin k_2\boldsymbol{d} = 0 \qquad \cos k_2\boldsymbol{d} = 1$$

and Eqs. B.10 and B.11 become

$$A\,[K_e(1 - \cos k_1\boldsymbol{d}) + L_e(1 - \cos k_1\boldsymbol{d}) - 2\pi^2\nu^2 m] = 0$$
$$B\,[L_e(1 - \cos k_1\boldsymbol{d}) - 2\pi^2\nu^2 m] = 0$$

which give the following ν vs. k characteristics:

$$\nu_{e1} = \frac{1}{\pi} \sqrt{\frac{K_e + L_e}{m}} \sin \frac{k_1\boldsymbol{d}}{2} \tag{B.13}$$

$$\nu_{e2} = \frac{1}{\pi} \sqrt{\frac{L_e}{m}} \sin \frac{k_1\boldsymbol{d}}{2} \tag{B.13'}$$

for a [10] direction in k space.

The results for a [01] direction ($k_1 = 0$) are entirely similar:

$$\nu_{e1} = \frac{1}{\pi} \sqrt{\frac{K_e + L_e}{m}} \sin \frac{k_2\boldsymbol{d}}{2} \tag{B.14}$$

$$\nu_{e2} = \frac{1}{\pi} \sqrt{\frac{L_e}{m}} \sin \frac{k_2\boldsymbol{d}}{2} \tag{B.14'}$$

for a [01] direction in k space.

On the other hand, if $k_1 = k_2 = k_0$, that is, the direction is [11], then Eqs. B.10 and B.11 become

$$A\,[K_e(1 - \cos k_0\boldsymbol{d}) + L_e(1 - \cos^2 k_0\boldsymbol{d}) - 2\pi^2\nu^2 m]$$
$$+ B\,[L_e \sin^2 k_0\boldsymbol{d}] = 0$$

$$A\,[L_e \sin^2 k_0\boldsymbol{d}] + B\,[K_e(1 - \cos k_0\boldsymbol{d})$$
$$+ L_e(1 - \cos^2 k_0\boldsymbol{d}) - 2\pi^2\nu^2 m] = 0$$

which, upon applying Eq. B.12, lead to two identical or degenerate solutions for ν

$$\nu_{e1} = \nu_{e2} = \nu_e = \frac{1}{\pi} \sqrt{\frac{K_e}{m}} \sin \frac{k_0\boldsymbol{d}}{2} \tag{B.15}$$

indicating that the two frequency surfaces in ν–k space must come together along the diagonal directions in the square lattice.

It is clear from all of these particular solutions, and also from the general equation (Eq. B.12), that the frequency is periodic in $k_1 d$ and $k_2 d$ just as it is for the one-dimensional case. Indeed, for certain directions of propagation (e.g., [10], [01̄], [11]), maxima in both ν_{e1} and ν_{e2} are reached when

$$\frac{k_1 d}{2} = \frac{\pi}{2} \qquad \text{or} \qquad \frac{k_2 d}{2} = \frac{\pi}{2}$$

corresponding to values of the wave vector with components

$$k_1 = \frac{\pi}{d} \qquad \text{and} \qquad k_2 = \frac{\pi}{d}$$

A wave propagating in the [11] direction, however, has a maximum or cut-off frequency when the components of $\mathbf{k}$ are each π/d, or when $\mathbf{k}$ has a magnitude

$$k = |\mathbf{k}| = \sqrt{k_1^2 + k_2^2} = \sqrt{2}\,\pi/d$$

A representation of the two frequency–wave vector surfaces for elastic-displacement waves in the square lattice is presented in Figure B.4, where the elastic-interaction constant, L_e, between next-nearest

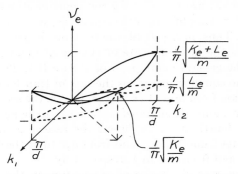

Fig. B.4. The dependence of frequency, ν, on wave vector, k, for an elastic-displacement wave in an infinite two-dimensional square lattice of spacing, d. The wave vector, $\mathbf{k}$, has components k_1 and k_2. Solid lines show ν_1 surface; dashed lines, ν_2 surface. Note that both surfaces coincide along the projected diagonal direction, where $k_1 = k_2$.

(second) neighbors is assumed to be smaller than that between nearest (first) neighbors, such that $K_e \cong 10L_e$.

After this fairly detailed consideration of elastic-displacement waves in a two-dimensional square lattice, we turn to a consideration of momentum or particle waves in the same lattice. The differential equations of motion for the n,r point are now written using a momentum transfer constant, $\mathbf{K}_p$, for nearest neighbors, and a corresponding constant, $\mathbf{L}_p$, for next-nearest neighbors. Further, the equations are in terms of the velocities of the masses rather than the displacements. These equations are

$$\frac{\partial(mu_{n,r})}{\partial t} = [\mathbf{K}_p(u_{n-1,r} - u_{n,r})] - [\mathbf{K}_p(u_{n,r} - u_{n+1,r})]$$
$$+ [\mathbf{L}_p(u_{n-1,r+1} - u_{n,r})] - [\mathbf{L}_p(u_{n,r} - u_{n+1,r-1})]$$
$$+ [\mathbf{L}_p(u_{n-1,r-1} - u_{n,r})] - [\mathbf{L}_p(u_{n,r} - u_{n+1,r+1})]$$

$$\text{(B.16)}$$

$$\frac{\partial(mv_{n,r})}{\partial t} = [\mathbf{K}_p(v_{n,r-1} - v_{n,r})] - [\mathbf{K}_p(v_{n,r} - v_{n,r+1})]$$
$$+ [\mathbf{L}_p(v_{n+1,r-1} - v_{n,r})] - [\mathbf{L}_p(v_{n,r} - v_{n-1,r+1})]$$
$$+ [\mathbf{L}_p(v_{n-1,r-1} - v_{n,r})] - [\mathbf{L}_p(v_{n,r} - v_{n+1,r+1})] \qquad \text{(B.17)}$$

where $u_{n,r}$ and $v_{n,r}$ are the x and y components of velocity of point (n,r), etc. Before simplifying these equations, we first consider them term-by-term. Thus, in Eq. B.16, the term on the left of the equality sign represents the net time rate of change of momentum in the x direction at the general point (n,r) of Figure B.1. The first term to the right of the equality sign gives the rate of transfer of momentum in the x direction from mass 1 $(n-1,r)$ *to* n,r; the second term gives the x-direction momentum transfer *from* n,r to point 5 $(n+1,r)$; the third and fourth terms represent the rate of x-component momentum transfer from 2 to n,r and from n,r to 6; the fifth and sixth from 8 to n,r and from n,r to 4, respectively.

The net time rate of change of momentum in the y direction of n,r is similarly represented by the differences between rates of momentum transfer to n,r from masses 6, 7, and 8, and the rate of momentum transfer away from n,r to masses 2, 3, and 4, as given in Eq. B.17. In both differential equations, a physical assumption is implicit; that is, that momentum transfer from a single mass (n,r)

can take place simultaneously to several masses in the lattice (e.g., three in this next-nearest-neighbor approximation). *This assumption is not correct*, but, in order to demonstrate this fact, one can first develop some results of the assumption and then demonstrate that it leads to both mathematical and physical contradictions.

These equations (B.16 and B.17) constitute statements of the law of conservation of momentum between n,r and its nearest and next-nearest neighbors (the rest of the masses in the lattice are neglected in this approximation). Unlike the situation for elastic-displacement waves, *there is no coupling between x and y components of velocity* since momentum must be independently conserved in each direction. Here, we have a fundamental difference between the two kinds of waves. Each component of the particle momentum wave, therefore, proceeds independently of the other.

The absence of coupling between u and v makes the solutions of the differential equations B.16 and B.17 relatively simple. Collecting terms and rearranging these equations, we have

$$m \frac{\partial u_{n,r}}{\partial t} = \mathbf{K}_p(u_{n+1,r} + u_{n-1,r} - 2u_{n,r}) + \mathbf{L}_p(u_{n-1,r+1}$$
$$+ u_{n+1,r-1} + u_{n-1,r-1} + u_{n+1,r+1} - 4u_{n,r}) \qquad \text{(B.16}')$$

$$m \frac{\partial v_{n,r}}{\partial t} = \mathbf{K}_p(v_{n,r+1} + v_{n,r-1} - 2v_{n,r}) + \mathbf{L}_p(v_{n+1,r-1}$$
$$+ v_{n-1,r+1} + v_{n-1,r-1} + v_{n+1,r+1} - 4v_{n,r}) \qquad \text{(B.17}')$$

Possible solutions for $u_{n,r}$ and $v_{n,r}$ are

$$u_{n,r} = C e^{-i(2\pi\nu t - k_1 n\boldsymbol{d} - k_2 r\boldsymbol{d})} \qquad \text{(B.18)}$$

$$v_{n,r} = D e^{-i(2\pi\nu t - k_1 n\boldsymbol{d} - k_2 r\boldsymbol{d})} \qquad \text{(B.19)}$$

These solutions may be differentiated and substituted into Eqs. B.16$'$ and B.17$'$ (with appropriate values of n,r) to give the necessary dependence of ν on k for the solutions to be valid. The results are

$$\nu_{p1} = \frac{2K_p}{\pi m} \sin^2\left(\frac{k_1\boldsymbol{d}}{2}\right) + \frac{2L_p}{\pi m}(1 - \cos k_1\boldsymbol{d} \cos k_2\boldsymbol{d}) \qquad \text{(B.20)}$$

$$\nu_{p2} = \frac{2K_p}{\pi m} \sin^2\left(\frac{k_2\boldsymbol{d}}{2}\right) + \frac{2L_p}{\pi m}(1 - \cos k_2\boldsymbol{d} \cos k_1\boldsymbol{d}) \qquad \text{(B.21)}$$

where we let $\mathbf{K}_p = iK_p$ and $\mathbf{L}_p = iL_p$ to obtain real, positive values of ν as in the one-dimensional case. Equations B.20 and B.21 give two values of frequency for each pair of k_1, k_2 values, and are relatively simple in contrast to the corresponding general quadratic equation in ν^2 (Eq. B.12) for elastic-displacement waves.

We see that both ν_{p1} and ν_{p2} are periodic in the wave-vector components (k_1, k_2) (i.e., have a period of 2π in $k_1\mathbf{d}$ or $k_2\mathbf{d}$), just as for elastic waves. Special solutions for particular directions in k space can also be obtained, for example, $k_2 = 0$ ([10] direction).

$$\nu_{p1} = \frac{2}{\pi m} \ (K_p + 2L_p) \ \sin^2 \left(\frac{k_1\mathbf{d}}{2} \right) \qquad \text{(B.22)}$$

$$\nu_{p2} = \frac{4L_p}{\pi m} \sin^2 \left(\frac{k_1\mathbf{d}}{2} \right) \qquad \text{(B.22$'$)}$$

Similarly, for $k_1 = 0$ ([01] direction), we get

$$\nu_{p1} = \frac{4L_p}{\pi m} \sin^2 \left(\frac{k_2\mathbf{d}}{2} \right) \qquad \text{(B.23)}$$

$$\nu_{p2} = \frac{2}{\pi m} \ (K_p + 2L_p) \ \sin^2 \left(\frac{k_2\mathbf{d}}{2} \right) \qquad \text{(B.23$'$)}$$

Equations B.22 and B.23 may be compared to Eqs. B.13 and B.14 for elastic waves and some similarities noticed. On the other hand, if $k_1 = k_2 = k_0$ ([11] direction in k space), we find that

$$\nu_p = \nu_{p1} = \nu_{p2} = \frac{2K_p}{\pi m} \sin^2 \left(\frac{k_0\mathbf{d}}{2} \right) + \frac{2L_p}{\pi m} \sin^2 k_0\mathbf{d} \qquad \text{(B.24)}$$

or, if we express ν_p as a function of the magnitude of the wave vector in the direction of propagation, k, instead of the component, k_0, we have

$$\nu_p = \frac{2K_p}{\pi m} \sin^2 \left(\frac{k\mathbf{d}}{2\sqrt{2}} \right) + \frac{2L_p}{\pi m} \sin^2 \left(\frac{k\mathbf{d}}{\sqrt{2}} \right) \qquad \text{(B.25)}$$

since $k = \sqrt{2} \ k_0$ for the [11] direction. The variations of ν_p with k along a [10] and [11] direction in k space are shown in Figures B.5 and B.6. The corresponding variations of ν_e with k for elastic waves are also indicated by the dashed curves in these figures. We notice that the frequencies reach a maximum at values of $k = \pi/d$ and $k = \sqrt{2}\,\pi/d$ for the elastic waves, but that this is not necessarily the case for a particle wave proceeding in the [11] direction. The partial derivative of ν_p with respect to k is zero at $\sqrt{2}\,\pi/d$, but ν_p is not always a maximum at this point; the exact shape of the ν_p vs. k curve will be dependent on the relative values of K_p and L_p for the lattice. The fact that $\partial\nu_p/\partial k$ is zero at $k = \sqrt{2}\,\pi/d$ is readily seen by differentiating Eq. B.25, from which

$$\frac{\partial \nu_p}{\partial t} = \frac{2K_p}{\pi m} \cdot \frac{d}{2\sqrt{2}} \sin\left(\frac{kd}{2\sqrt{2}}\right) \cos\left(\frac{kd}{2\sqrt{2}}\right)$$

$$+ \frac{2L_p}{\pi m} \cdot \frac{d}{\sqrt{2}} \sin\left(\frac{kd}{\sqrt{2}}\right) \cos\left(\frac{kd}{\sqrt{2}}\right) \qquad \text{(B.26)}$$

$$\frac{\partial \nu_p}{\partial t} = 0 \qquad \text{when} \qquad k = \sqrt{2}\,\pi/d$$

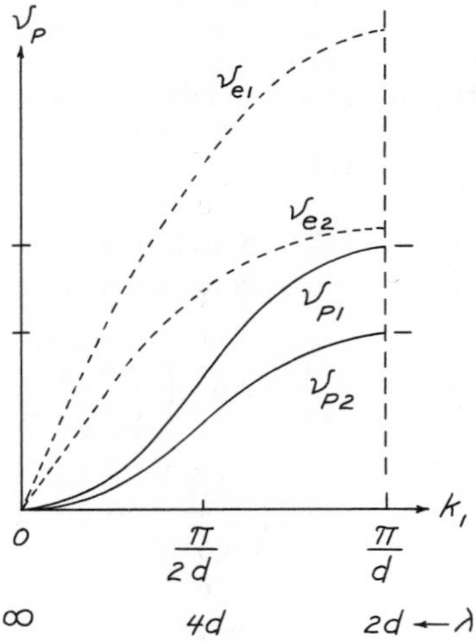

Fig. B.5. Frequency vs. wave vector curves for a particle momentum wave in an infinite two-dimensional square lattice of spacing, d, where multiple momentum transfer is assumed and the direction is [10]. Dashed lines show corresponding frequency characteristics for an elastic-displacement wave in the same direction. The existence of two $\nu-k$ branches for particle waves is not physically possible, but results from the incorrect assumption that one mass can simultaneously transfer momentum to two or more masses in the lattice.

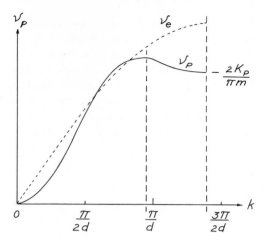

Fig. B.6. Frequency vs. wave vector curve for a particle momentum wave in an infinite two-dimensional square lattice of spacing, d, where multiple momentum transfer is assumed and the direction is [11]. Dashed line shows the corresponding curve for an elastic-displacement wave in the same direction. Particle-wave curve is drawn for the case where $L_p = K_p/2$, and has a maximum at $k \cong 0.94\, \pi/d$ and a minimum at $k = \sqrt{2}\, \pi/d$. Since multiple momentum transfer is not possible, however, this particle-wave curve is incorrect, as explained in the text.

In order to determine whether a maximum or minimum exists at $k = \sqrt{2}\, \pi/d$, we examine the second derivative,

$$\frac{\partial^2 \nu_p}{\partial k^2} = \frac{K_p}{\pi m}\left[\frac{d^2}{4}\cos^2\left(\frac{kd}{2\sqrt{2}}\right) - \sin^2\left(\frac{kd}{2\sqrt{2}}\right)\right]$$

$$+ \frac{L_p}{\pi m}\left[d^2\cos^2\left(\frac{kd}{\sqrt{2}}\right) - \sin^2\left(\frac{kd}{\sqrt{2}}\right)\right] \qquad \text{(B.27)}$$

which has the value, at $k = \sqrt{2}\, \pi/d$, of

$$\left.\frac{\partial^2 \nu_p}{\partial k^2}\right|_{k=\sqrt{2}\,k/d} = \frac{d^2}{\pi m}\left[L_p - \frac{K_p}{4}\right] \qquad \text{(B.28)}$$

$$= \text{negative if } L_p < K_p/4 \;(\text{maximum})$$

$$= \text{positive if } L_p > K_p/4 \;(\text{minimum})$$

The particle-wave curves of Figure B.6 are drawn for the case where $L_p = K_p/2$ and, hence, a minimum occurs at $k = \sqrt{2}\,\pi/d$. The exact position of the maximum in the ν vs. k curve for the [11] direction can be determined for particular relative values of K_p and L_p. Thus, for the curve of Figure B.6 where $L_p = K_p/2$, the expression for the first derivative of ν with respect to k (Eq. B.26) becomes:

$$\frac{\partial \nu_p}{\partial k} = \frac{K_p}{\pi m}\frac{d}{\sqrt{2}}\left[\sin\left(\frac{kd}{2\sqrt{2}}\right)\cos\left(\frac{kd}{2\sqrt{2}}\right) + \sin\left(\frac{kd}{\sqrt{2}}\right)\cos\left(\frac{kd}{\sqrt{2}}\right)\right] \text{(B.26')}$$

The term in brackets is of the form,

$$\sin\frac{a}{2}\cos\frac{a}{2} + \sin a \cos a$$

which, by substitution of the proper trigonometric identity, becomes

$$\frac{\sin a}{2} + \sin a \cos a = \sin a\left(\frac{1}{2} + \cos a\right)$$

so that it will be equal to zero if

$$\cos a = -\frac{1}{2}$$

or

$$a = \frac{2\pi}{3}\text{ radians} \qquad (120°)$$

Therefore, the maximum occurs at a value of k given by

$$\frac{kd}{\sqrt{2}} = \frac{2\pi}{3}$$

or

$$k\text{ (max)} = \sqrt{2}\,\frac{2}{3}\frac{\pi}{d} \cong 0.94\ \pi/d$$

Solutions to Eqs. B.20 and B.21 for other directions in k space can also be obtained, and frequency surfaces for particle waves constructed as functions of k_1, k_2, such as those of Figure B.4 for elastic-displacement waves.

Before obtaining additional solutions for two dimensions or extending the differential equations for particle waves to take into account a three-dimensional (cubic) lattice, we note certain fundamental difficulties with the results based on the picture of two-dimensional momentum transfer inherent in the approach used so far. We have used a method analogous to that outlined for elastic waves in which "nearest" and "next-nearest" neighbors to a mass in the lattice are assumed to simultaneously interact with the mass. In both the elastic- and particle-wave cases, the effect of next-nearest-neighbor interactions is to produce, in general, two distinct frequency-wave vector characteristics or branches, such as shown for the [10] direction in Figure B.5. Now this is easily explained for elastic-displacement waves, where the connection between frequency and wavelength is through the phase velocity, c_s,

$$\nu_e = c_s / \lambda$$

and two possible values of ν_e for one λ can arise from different values of c_s, such as those for transverse and longitudinal sound waves, for example. The existence of two frequencies for a single value of wavelength (or wave vector, k) for a particle wave at low values of k cannot be explained on the same basis, however. The relation between energy, E, and frequency, ν, for a particle wave has already been mentioned (i.e., $E = h\nu$), and the existence of two frequencies for a particle wave at *low values of* k implies that *one* free particle could have simultaneously *two* energies. Since the particle energy, in turn, depends on velocity, this amounts to saying that a single free particle has two different velocities at the same time. The same contradiction can be brought out by noting that two ν vs. k curves result also in two different values of $d\nu/dk$ and, thus, group velocity, v_g, at a given value of k or λ. This, of course, is not possible according to the de Broglie relation, where each particle wavelength, λ, of a field-free particle has associated with it only *one* group and one particle velocity, viz:

$$v_g = v = h/m\lambda$$

Hence, we again see that the existence of two branches in the frequency–wave vector characteristic for particle waves in a lattice leads to the erroneous conclusion that one particle can simultaneously have two velocities. We emphasize that the two separate branches exist even at small values of k (long wavelengths), where the particle waves must behave as if they were in a field-free region. In fact, this necessary boundary condition itself points out the difficulty in another way. That is, if we attempt to evaluate K_p and L_p by requiring that the expressions for ν as a function of k reduce to the field-free relation

$$\nu = \frac{\hbar}{4\pi m} \cdot k^2$$

for small k independent of direction in the lattice, we replace the sine by its argument, in each of Eqs. B.22, B.22′, and B.25, to get

$$\nu_{p1} = \frac{L_p \cdot d^2}{\pi m} \cdot k_1^2 = \frac{\hbar}{4\pi m} \cdot k_1^2$$

$$\nu_{p2} = \frac{(K_p + L_p)\, d^2}{2\pi m} \cdot k_1^2 = \frac{\hbar}{4\pi m} \cdot k_1^2$$

$$\nu_p = \frac{(K_p + 4L_p)\, d^2}{4\pi m} \cdot k^2 = \frac{\hbar}{4\pi m} \cdot k^2$$

for small values of k. The above expressions lead to the following *incompatible* equations for K_p and L_p:

$$K_p + 4L_p = \hbar/d^2$$

$$K_p + L_p = \tfrac{1}{2}(\hbar/d^2)$$

$$L_p = \tfrac{1}{4}(\hbar/d^2)$$

The last two of these equations require that K_p and L_p have the same value, $\hbar/4d^2$, but this requirement, combined with the first equation, leads to a value for K_p of $\hbar/5d^2$, for example. *All of these remarks demonstrate that the differential equations (Eqs. B.16 and B.17) selected to describe momentum transfer in the square lattice of Figure B.1 are physically incorrect descriptions of the process.* These equations were set up partly by analogy with the elastic-wave equations, of course, and provide for simultaneous transfer of momentum components, not only between masses lined up in the component direction, but between other masses as well. Thus, Eq. B.16 is equivalent to the situation depicted in Figure B.7a, where x components of momentum are somehow transferred from masses 2, 1, and 8 to n,r and from n,r to 4, 5, and 6. This view of the momentum-transfer process in a two-dimensional lattice leads to the physical and mathematical contradictions already discussed. Hence, we are forced to revise this concept of the two-dimensional momentum-transfer process. Instead of supposing that part of the x component of momentum of n,r can be simultaneously transferred to three vertically aligned masses in the lattice, as in Figure B.7a, we instead require that such momentum transfer take place only between n,r and No. 5. That is, *momentum transfer in any particular direction in a lattice takes place only between masses (atoms) lined up in that direction.*

This result is a direct consequence of what may be called the principle of

one mass, one velocity

which is taken as a fundamental postulate, not even requiring a Supreme Court opinion in this case. Thus, if we agree that a single mass can have only one velocity at any instant, and that the momentum transfer takes place in the lattice via the mechanism of particle-wave propagation, the result italicized above follows.

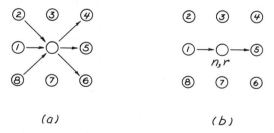

(a)   (b)

Fig. B.7. Diagram (a) depicting multiple (simultaneous) momentum transfer from a single mass to three other masses in a two-dimensional square lattice. In reality, the mass (n,r) can transfer momentum to only one mass at a time, as shown in (b). The assumption of simultaneous multiple momentum transfer, as shown in (a), leads to both physical and mathematical contradictions, as discussed in the text.

If we now consider a general point (n,r) in the two-dimensional lattice of Figure B.1, we can write separate and completely uncoupled equations for various directions in the lattice, viz.,

[10] direction $v = v_x, \; v_y = 0$

$$m \, \frac{\partial v_{n,r}}{\partial t} = \mathbf{K}_p (v_{n+1,r} + v_{n-1,r} - 2v_{n,r}) \qquad \text{(B.29)}$$

[11] direction $v = v_x^2 + v_y^2, \; v_x = v_y$

$$m \, \frac{\partial v_{n,r}}{\partial t} = \mathbf{K}_p' (v_{n+1,r+1} + v_{n-1,r-1} - 2v_{n,r}) \qquad \text{(B.30)}$$

[21] direction $v = v_x^2 + v_y^2, \; v_x = 2v_y$

$$m \, \frac{\partial v_{n,r}}{\partial t} = \mathbf{K}_p'' (v_{n+2,r+1} + v_{n-2,r-1} - 2v_{n,r}) \qquad \text{(B.31)}$$

etc.

The primes on $\mathbf{K}_p$ indicate that the momentum transfer constant may have different values for different directions in the lattice. These equations all lead to single-valued curves of ν vs. k, where k is in the specified direction in the lattice, and the solution for velocity is of the form,

$$v_{n,r} = A e^{-i(2\pi \nu t - k_1 n \boldsymbol{d} - k_2 r \boldsymbol{d})}$$

A single example will suffice to illustrate the general result. Thus, in the [11] direction the condition on ν, for the above solution to be valid for Eq. B.30, is

$$\nu_p = \frac{2K_p'}{\pi m} \sin^2 \left(\frac{(k_1 + k_2) \, \boldsymbol{d}}{2} \right) \qquad \text{(B.32)}$$

but in this direction,

$$k_1 = k_2 = k/\sqrt{2}$$

so that

$$(k_1 + k_2) \, \boldsymbol{d} = k \boldsymbol{d}'$$

where

$$\boldsymbol{d}' = \sqrt{2} \, \boldsymbol{d}$$

is the lattice spacing in the [11] direction. Then,

$$\nu_p = \frac{2K_p'}{\pi m} \sin^2 \left(\frac{k d'}{2} \right) \tag{B.33}$$

and the requirement that Eq. B.33 reduce to that for a free particle at small values of k leads to a momentum transfer constant, K_p' (for the [11] direction), of

$$K_p' = \frac{\hbar}{2(d')^2} \tag{B.34}$$

These results can, in fact, be generalized for any direction in the square lattice, so that it is always true that

$$\nu_p = \frac{2K_{pj}}{\pi m} \sin^2 \left(\frac{k d_j}{2} \right) \tag{B.35}$$

and

$$K_{pj} = \frac{\hbar}{2d_j^2} \tag{B.36}$$

where d_j is the distance between atoms in the lattice for the particular direction chosen.

It is now not necessary to carry out details of the elastic- and particle-wave calculations for a three-dimensional (cubic lattice) like those demonstrated for two dimensions. Instead, we merely cite the results. These calculations were first carried out for elastic waves by Born and von Karman[1] and have been clearly described by Smith.[2] The principal effect of considering a third dimension is that three differential equations, like B.1 and B.2, now appear in terms of the x,y,z components of displacement of a general point (n,r,s), and *six* nearest neighbors as well as *twelve* next-nearest neighbors must be taken into account. Hence, additional terms appear in the corresponding differential equations, including both y and z terms, for example, in the differential equation for the x component of displacement. Solutions of the form

$$\begin{aligned} x_{n,r,s} &= A e^{-i(2\pi\nu t - k_1 n d - k_2 r d - k_3 s d)} \\ y_{n,r,s} &= B e^{-i(2\pi\nu t - k_1 n d - k_2 r d - k_3 s d)} \\ z_{n,r,s} &= C e^{-i(2\pi\nu t - k_1 n d - k_2 r d - k_3 s d)} \end{aligned} \tag{B.37}$$

can then be found where the constants A, B, and C are given in terms of three simultaneous homogeneous equations, like Eqs. B.10 and B.11. The necessary condition for a solution to exist for this set of three equations is again that the (third-order) determinant of the coefficients vanish. This condition leads to a cubic equation for ν^2, which can be solved for any particular direction (k_1,k_2,k_3) in k space, with the general result that three separate ν vs. k characteristics are found for a given direction. Of course, relative values of K_e and L_e must be assumed, and the calculations are, in any case, tedious.

An extension of this same type of approach to particle waves results in three uncoupled differential equations in the x,y,z components of velocity (u,v,w), similar to Eqs. B.16 and B.17, but with additional terms taking into account possible momentum transfers to and from the general point (n,r,s) and the added neighbors. Solutions to these differential equations are of the form,

$$u_{n,r,s} = De^{-i(2\pi\nu t - k_1 n\boldsymbol{d} - k_2 r\boldsymbol{d} - k_3 s\boldsymbol{d})}$$

$$v_{n,r,s} = Ee^{-i(2\pi\nu t - k_1 n\boldsymbol{d} - k_2 r\boldsymbol{d} - k_3 s\boldsymbol{d})}$$

$$w_{n,r,s} = Fe^{-i(2\pi\nu t - k_1 n\boldsymbol{d} - k_2 r\boldsymbol{d} - k_3 s\boldsymbol{d})} \tag{B.38}$$

and lead to *three different* ν vs. k characteristics for any general direction (k_1,k_2,k_3) in k space. Now we have already demonstrated that there can be only one ν vs. k characteristic for a particle wave and, therefore, any assumptions leading to three such characteristics must be just as invalid as those leading to two. In fact, the principle of

one mass, one velocity

clearly requires that momentum transfer from the point (n,r,s) in a three-dimensional lattice can only take place to one mass at a time, and not simultaneously to five, as would be required if three ν vs. k characteristics could exist.

The final outcome of this discussion, therefore, is that the results for particle-wave propagation in a one-dimensional row lattice apply directly to particle waves in a three-dimensional lattice, where the periodic spacing, $\boldsymbol{d}$, between masses in the row simply must be replaced by the periodic spacing, $\boldsymbol{d}_j$, between lattice masses in any particular direction, $\mathbf{k}$, chosen in the three-dimensional lattice. Hence, the ν vs. k dependence and the value of the momentum transfer constant, K_p, can be written at once for any direction in any lattice.

A few examples for cubic lattices of spacing, d, follow:

Cubic lattice, $\langle 100 \rangle$ directions with spacing, d

$$\nu_p = \frac{2K_p}{\pi m} \sin^2 \left(\frac{kd}{2} \right)$$

and

$$K_p = \frac{\hbar}{2d^2}$$

whence

$$\nu_p = \frac{\hbar}{\pi m d^2} \sin^2 \left(\frac{kd}{2} \right)$$

Cubic lattice, $\langle 110 \rangle$ directions with spacing, $\sqrt{2}d$

$$K_p = \frac{\hbar}{4d^2}$$

whence

$$\nu_p = \frac{\hbar}{2\pi m d^2} \sin^2 \left(\frac{k\sqrt{2}\,d}{2} \right)$$

Cubic lattice, $\langle 111 \rangle$ directions with spacing, $\sqrt{3}d$

$$K_p = \frac{\hbar}{6d^2}$$

whence

$$\nu_p = \frac{\hbar}{3\pi m d^2} \sin^2 \left(\frac{k\sqrt{3}\,d}{2} \right)$$

fcc lattice, $\langle 100 \rangle$ directions with spacing, d

$$K_p = \frac{\hbar}{2d^2}$$

$$\nu_p = \frac{\hbar}{\pi m d^2} \sin^2 \left(\frac{kd}{2} \right)$$

fcc lattice, $\langle 110 \rangle$ directions with spacing, $d/\sqrt{2}$

$$K_p = \frac{\hbar}{d^2}$$

$$\nu_p = \frac{2\hbar}{\pi m d^2} \sin^2\left(\frac{kd}{2\sqrt{2}}\right)$$

fcc lattice, $\langle 111 \rangle$ directions with spacing, $\sqrt{3}d$

$$K_p = \frac{\hbar}{6d^2}$$

$$\nu_p = \frac{\hbar}{3\pi m d^2} \sin^2\left(\frac{k\sqrt{3}\,d}{2}\right)$$

fcc lattice, $\langle 211 \rangle$ directions with spacing, $\sqrt{3/2} \cdot d$

$$K_p = \frac{\hbar}{3d^2}$$

$$\nu_p = \frac{2\hbar}{3\pi m d^2} \sin^2\left(\frac{k\sqrt{3}\,d}{2\sqrt{2}}\right)$$

bcc lattice, $\langle 100 \rangle$ directions with spacing, d

$$K_p = \frac{\hbar}{2d^2}$$

$$\nu_p = \frac{\hbar}{\pi m d^2} \sin^2\left(\frac{kd}{2}\right)$$

bcc lattice, $\langle 111 \rangle$ directions with spacing, $\sqrt{3}\,d/2$

$$K_p = \frac{2\hbar}{3d^2}$$

$$\nu_p = \frac{4\hbar}{3\pi m d^2} \sin^2\left(\frac{k\sqrt{3}\,d}{4}\right)$$

etc.

The momentum transfer constant for any lattice will be largest in the direction of closest spacing, so that we expect slip to occur most readily in this direction. As mentioned before, this is in accordance with all experimental evidence.

REFERENCES

1. M. Born and T. von Karman, *Z. Phys.* **13**, 297 (1912); **14**, 15 (1913).
2. R. A. Smith, *Wave Mechanics of Crystalline Solids*, Wiley, New York, 1961.

APPENDIX C

FREQUENCY SPECTRUM FOR PERIODIC BOUNDARY CONDITIONS

In Chapter II, it is stated that the particle-wave frequency spectrum arising from periodic boundary conditions leads to results such as those from the spectrum of a finite lattice or segment. To see how this comes about, we recall that for identical (but nonzero) values of velocity at periodic spacing, Nd, in a lattice, the ν_p, k relation was (Eqs. 2.6 and 2.19),

$$\nu_p = \frac{2K_p}{\pi m} \sin^2\left(\frac{kd}{2}\right) \tag{C.1}$$

where

$$k = \pm q 2\pi / Nd$$

$$q = 1, 2, 3 \ldots (N-1)/2$$

Hence

$$\nu_{pq} = \nu_1 \sin^2\left(\frac{q\pi}{N}\right) \tag{C.2}$$

Differentiating Eq. C.2 with respect to q yields

$$d\nu_{pq} = \nu_1 \frac{2\pi}{N} \sin\left(\frac{q\pi}{N}\right) \cos\left(\frac{q\pi}{N}\right) dq \tag{C.3}$$

and recalling that, in general, $Z_p(\nu) = dq/d\nu_p$ (Eq. 2.20), we find the frequency distribution function, $Z_p'(\nu)$, to be

$$Z_p'(\nu) = \frac{N}{2\pi\nu_1 \sin\left(\frac{q\pi}{N}\right) \cos\left(\frac{q\pi}{N}\right)} \tag{C.4}$$

This expression, in turn, can be written in terms of $\nu_p \equiv \nu_{pq}$ by means of Eq. C.2, so that

$$Z'_p(\nu) = \frac{N}{2\pi \nu_1^{1/2} \nu_p^{1/2} \cos\,(\arcsin \sqrt{\nu_p/\nu_1})} \tag{C.5}$$

But there are an equal number of modes for waves propagating in each of *two* directions for the running particle waves arising from periodic boundary conditions. Thus, the function of Eq. C.5 must be multiplied by two to get the total distribution function or density of modes. Then,

$$2Z'_p(\nu) = Z_p(\nu) \tag{C.6}$$

where $Z_p(\nu)$ is as given in Eq. 2.24 of Chapter II. Hence, the total distribution function (envelope) is the same in both cases, although the actual details of the spacing between individual modes is different, as pointed out in Chapter II.

APPENDIX D

CALCULATION OF OSCILLATING FORCES AND TORQUES ON LATTICE SEGMENTS DURING PARTICLE-WAVE PROPAGATION

In Chapter II, brief mention was made of the existence of net oscillating translational forces and net oscillating torques resulting from particle-wave propagation along a crystal made up of finite lattice segments. In this Appendix, some additional details of the calculation of these forces and torques are given.

The progress of a particle wave through a lattice subjects each mass (atom) to an instantaneous force equal to the time rate of change of momentum at each mass site at any particular time. Using the expression for the velocity of a general nth lattice mass in a finite segment of length, Nd, we have, from Chapter II,

$$v_n(t) = B_1 e^{-i2\pi \nu_p t} \, 2i \sin kn\boldsymbol{d} \qquad \text{(D.1)}$$
$$\text{(2.3)}$$

so that $\partial v_n / \partial t$ can be calculated as

$$\frac{\partial v_n}{\partial t} = 4\pi B_1 \nu \sin kn\boldsymbol{d} \, e^{-i2\pi \nu t} \qquad \text{(D.2)}$$

This means that the force on the general nth point is

$$f_{pn}(t) = m \frac{\partial v_n}{\partial t} = 4\pi m B_1 \nu \sin kn\boldsymbol{d} \, e^{-i2\pi \nu t} \qquad \text{(D.3)}$$
$$\text{(2.30)}$$

$$\nu = \nu_p = \frac{2K_p}{\pi m} \sin^2 \left(\frac{k\boldsymbol{d}}{2} \right) \qquad \text{(D.4)}$$

$$k = q\pi/N\boldsymbol{d}$$

$$q = 1, 2, 3 \ldots (N-1)$$

$$n = 0, 1, 2, 3 \ldots N$$

The force expression can also be written in terms of the q integers, as

$$f_{pn}(t) = \frac{4B_1\hbar}{d^2} \sin^2\left(\frac{q\pi}{2N}\right) \sin\left(\frac{q\pi n}{N}\right) e^{-i2\pi\nu_{pq}t} \qquad \text{(D.5)}$$

where

$$K_p = \hbar/2d^2$$

$$\nu_{pq} = \nu_1 \sin^2\left(\frac{q\pi}{2N}\right)$$

$$\nu_1 = \frac{h}{2m\pi^2 d^2}$$

$$q = 1, 2, 3 \ldots (N-1)$$

Thus, each mass (atom) in the lattice segment of length, $S = Nd$, will experience an oscillating force of frequency, ν_{pq}, as the particle-momentum wave propagates along the segment. Only certain discrete values of frequency for the oscillating force will occur, in accordance with Eq. 2.21, but, as a consequence of the shape of the frequency spectrum previously described, many of these frequencies will lie in the audio range (for $S \cong 10^{-4}$ cm). From Eq. D.5, we see at once that the amplitude of the oscillating force will vary along the segment length in a different fashion for different modes. At the ends, the force is always zero for all modes, but at the center, where $n = N/2$, the force will have a maximum amplitude for odd modes and zero amplitude for even modes. For low values of q, it is convenient to replace Eq. D.5 by the approximate relation,

$$f_{pn}(t) \cong \frac{B_1\hbar}{S^2} \pi^2 q^2 \sin\left(\frac{q\pi n}{N}\right) e^{-i2\pi\nu_{pq}t} \qquad \text{(D.6)}$$

$$q < N/9$$

For any mode, the variation of amplitude along the segment at a given time is easily calculated as a function of n/N. The results for the first four modes were shown in Figure 2.11. From Figure 2.11, it is apparent that there will be no net translational force on the segment as a whole for even modes, but for odd modes there will be a *net* oscillating translational force on the entire segment. Such a net force will tend to set into vibration the crystal sample as a whole, in much the same way that an external oscillating force (applied over some portion of the crystal) produces vibration. The value of the net amplitude for a long segment can be calculated for any mode by

$$A_q = \int_0^N f_{pn}(0)\, dn \qquad (D.7)$$

where we can use the approximate expression for $f_{pn}(0)$ of Eq. D.6 for low modes. Then

$$A_q \cong \frac{B_1 \hbar}{S^2}\, \pi q N \left(\cos \frac{q\pi n}{N} \right) \Bigg|_N^0$$

$$= \frac{B_1 h}{S^2}\, N q \qquad \begin{matrix} (D.8) \\ (2.32) \end{matrix}$$

$$q = 1, 3, 5, 7 \ldots$$

but

$$A_q = 0$$

$$q = 2, 4, 6, 8 \ldots$$

Therefore, an expression for the net oscillating force on an *entire* segment for any mode, q, of the particle-momentum transfer wave can be written as

$$f_q(t) \cong A_q\, e^{-i2\pi \nu_{pq} t}$$

$$\cong \frac{B_1 h}{N d^2}\, q e^{-i2\pi \nu_{pq} t} \qquad \begin{matrix} (D.9) \\ (2.33) \end{matrix}$$

$$q = 1, 3, 5 \ldots < N/9$$

An estimate of the magnitude of A_q for the lowest mode ($q = 1$) gives (for $Nd \cong 10^{-4}$ cm and $d \cong 3 \times 10^{-8}$ cm)

$$A_1 \cong B_1 \cdot 2.2 \times 10^{-15} \text{ dynes}$$

The amplitude of the particle wave (velocity) is given by B_1, whose value will depend on the external unidirectional load applied to the sample. In accordance with our previous discussion, however, B_1 cannot be greater than about 10^3 cm/sec in most cases, setting an upper bound on A_q of

$$A_1 \leq 2 \times 10^{-12} \text{ dynes}$$

The average or mean-force amplitude per unit length along a segment 10^{-4} cm long then is

$$\bar{A}_1 \cong 2 \times 10^{-8} \text{ dynes/cm}$$

The mean amplitude over a unit area within the sample will depend on the number of segments in which a particle wave is simultaneously propagating. If *all* such segments are active, then there would be about 3×10^7 segments across a 1-cm wide strip, and the maximum possible mean *stress* amplitude would be

$$\bar{s}_{01} = 0.6 \text{ dynes/cm}^2$$

which is still a very small stress amplitude. We can still add another dimension, however, and estimate the mean amplitude of body force (force/volume) for a sample which will again be increased by a maximum possible (but very improbable) amount up to 3×10^7, to give

$$\bar{\tau}_{01} = 2 \times 10^7 \text{ dynes/cm}^3$$

We in no wise expect that such values of stress or force densities will ever prevail over large regions in the sample; but there is the possibility that such values may be reached on a local scale from place to place in the crystal.

We do expect, however, that very small amplitude audio-frequency sounds will accompany the plastic deformation of crystals, along with a set of vibrations in the range of 10^9 to 10^{10} cps. Since the process of plastic deformation by slip is of a jerky or discontinuous nature, as previously noted, we expect that the sounds should correlate with each deformation jump or process.

In discussing net translational forces on a segment, we noted that contributions from even modes are absent. This is not to say, however,

that the even modes do not contribute to the vibration of the crystal
as a whole. On the contrary, even modes will produce net oscillating
moments on the lattice segments giving rise to internal twisting or
torsional forces in the crystal. An expression for the net amplitude of
moment of force (torque) of the lattice segment about its midpoint
$(n = N/2)$ can be found from

$$M_q = \int_0^{N/2} f_{pn} \cdot (n - N/2) \cdot d \cdot dn + \int_{N/2}^N f_{pn} \cdot (n - N/2) \cdot d \cdot dn$$
$$\text{(D.10)}$$

$$= d \cdot \int_0^{N/2} f_{pn}\, n\, dn + d \cdot \int_{N/2}^N f_{pn}\, n\, dn$$

$$- \frac{Nd}{2} \cdot \int_0^{N/2} f_{pn}\, dn - \frac{Nd}{2} \cdot \int_{N/2}^N f_{pn}\, dn \qquad \text{(D.11)}$$

The first two integrals become, on substitution of f_{pn} from Eq. D.6,
of the form

$$\int x \sin x\, dx = \sin x - x \cos x$$

while the last two are of the form

$$\int \sin x\, dx = - \cos x$$

where $x = q\pi n/N$ is the variable. Upon proper substitution and
integration, one obtains, therefore, from Eq. D.11, the following:

$$M_q = \frac{B_1 h}{2\pi d} \left[-q\pi \cos q\pi \right] + \frac{B_1 h}{4d} \left[q(\cos q\pi - 1) \right]$$

$$= - \frac{B_1 h}{4d}\, q(\cos q\pi + 1) \qquad \text{(D.12)}$$

so that, for odd values of q,

$$M_q = 0$$

$$q = 1, 3, 5, 7 \ldots$$

and for even values of q,

$$M_q = -\frac{B_1 h}{2d} q$$

$$q = 2, 4, 6, 8 \ldots$$

where the negative sign merely indicates the direction of torque at $t = 0$. In fact, the time dependence of the net instantaneous or oscillating torque of the entire segment about the midpoint of the segment is, for any mode q,

$$T_q(t) = M_q \, e^{-i2\pi \nu_{pq} t}$$

$$= \frac{B_1 h}{4d} \, q (\cos q\pi + 1) \, e^{i2\pi \nu_{pq} t} \qquad \text{(D.13)}$$
$$\text{(2.34)}$$

$$q = 2, 4, 6, 8 \ldots < N/9$$

The amplitudes of these torques will again be very small for each segment, but, if groups of active segments are concentrated in a small region and happen to be in phase, some detectable vibrations from this source might occur. The most common frequencies will again be at the extremes of the particle-wave spectrum, i.e., around 10^3 to 10^4 cps and 10^9 to 10^{10} cps, because of the high density of modes in these regions.

We have used the approximate expression for f_{pn} from Eq. D.6, since our interest is chiefly in audio-frequency modes at the present. However, use of the exact expression for f_{pn}, given by Eq. D.5, will not alter the main results in any way; only the amplitude of the oscillating forces and torques will change slightly at higher values of q.

If running waves produced by periodic (nonzero) boundary conditions on $\nu_n(t)$ are considered, instead of standing waves, the oscillating force at a point, n, along a segment of length Nd is given by

$$f_{pn} = m \frac{\partial v_n}{\partial t}$$

$$f_{pn} = -\frac{2iB\hbar}{d^2} \sin^2 \left(\frac{q\pi}{N} \right) e^{i2\pi qn/N} e^{-i2\pi \nu_{pq} t} \qquad \text{(D.14)}$$

where

$$\nu_{pq} = \nu_1 \sin^2 \left(\frac{q\pi}{N} \right)$$

$$\nu_1 = \frac{h}{2m\pi^2 d^2}$$

$$n = 1, 2, 3 \ldots N$$

$$q = 1, 2, 3 \ldots (N - 1)/2$$

instead of Eq. D.5. Again, we see that each mass of a part of the lattice of length, $S = Nd$, experiences an oscillating force whose amplitude varies with position along the lattice. The exact variation is dependent on the mode, q, of the particle wave propagated as before; now, however, the amplitudes are not always zero at $n = 0$ and $n = N$. Without going into the details, we can state that net oscillating translational forces and net oscillating torques will occur periodically along the lattice sections of length, Nd, just as they did for standing waves.

APPENDIX E

LIST OF PRINCIPAL SYMBOLS USED

G	Elastic shear modulus
h	Planck's constant
P	Linear momentum
λ	Wavelength
m	Mass of a particle (atom)
v	Magnitude of particle velocity, $\mathbf{v}$
c	Propagation (phase) velocity of a wave
ψ	Magnitude of a wave at a particular time and location
ψ_0	Wave amplitude
ν	Wave frequency
v_g	Group velocity of a wave
n	An integer (1, 2, 3 . . . etc.) used to denote the position of a general nth atom in a row lattice
d	Magnitude of lattice spacing
d_1	Magnitude of smallest spacing between atoms in a crystal lattice (distance of closest approach)
E	Total energy
$\hbar$	$h/2\pi$
V	Potential energy
i	$\sqrt{-1}$, or sometimes the angle of incidence
∇^2	Differential operator, $\dfrac{\partial^2}{\partial x^2} + \dfrac{\partial^2}{\partial y^2} + \dfrac{\partial^2}{\partial z^2}$
Y	Average force per unit area (stress)
ζ	Number of atoms per cross-sectional area in a crystal
F	Force
p	Field-free parameter giving width pd of field-free region occupied by a field-free atom in a crystal lattice.
k	Magnitude $(2\pi/\lambda)$ of wave vector $\mathbf{k}$, or, in a few cases, Boltzman's constant

K_e Elastic interaction constant for central elastic forces between neighboring atoms in a crystal

$\mathbf{K}_p$ Complex momentum transfer constant or velocity interaction constant between atoms in a monatomic lattice

K_p Magnitude of $\mathbf{K}_p$

S Lattice segment length $(N\boldsymbol{d})$, or, in a few cases, entropy

q An integer $(1, 2, 3 \ldots$ etc.$)$

D Lattice dissociation energy per atom (equal to lattice cohesive or binding energy per atom)

U Kinetic energy

$\boldsymbol{c}_s$ A mean sound velocity for a cubic crystal defined by $c_s^2 = (c_{t1}^2 + c_{t2}^2 + c_l^2)/6$ where c_{t1}, c_{t2}, are orthogonal transverse sound velocities and c_l is the corresponding longitudinal sound velocity for the crystal.

ρ Density

Ω Orientation factor between external stress $\mathbf{Y}_0$ and a particular direction $\mathbf{d}$ (with spacing $\boldsymbol{d}_j$) in a crystal lattice

E Young's modulus

β Parabolic coefficient in stress–strain law

ξ Number of field-free particles per unit length in a particular direction in a crystal lattice

u_f Energy required for the formation of a field-free interlattice atom in a crystal

μ Coefficient of static friction

μ' Coefficient of kinetic friction

ϵ Strain

T Torque, or sometimes temperature

AUTHOR INDEX*

Italic numbers refer to pages in the Reference Sections.

SUBJECT INDEX

240

Coefficient, of elastic compliance, calculation of Young's modulus, 182, 183
of friction, kinetic, 140
static, 140
parabolic, stress–strain law, 181; see also Parabolic coefficients
of sliding friction, 139, 140
Compliance, dynamic mechanical, 45
elastic coefficient, 182, 183
Copper, acoustic emission of, 57, 58
free-flight impact of, 96
hypervelocity cratering of, 91
mosaic structure of, 43
single crystal directional effects, in hypervelocity cratering, 87–89
in sliding friction, 166, 167
Coulomb explanation of sliding friction, 141
Crater formation, in hypervelocity impact, 84
in polycrystals, 85–87
in single crystals, 87–89
threshold velocity for, 74, 81–83, 90–96
Critical angle, 142
Critical velocities, for free-flight impact, 95, 96
Crystal defects, 14, 184
Crystal mosaics, formation of, 177
size of, 42, 43, 179, 180
Cut-off frequency, 17, 18

Davisson-Germer experiment, 4
Defects, see Crystal defects, Initial defect state
Deformation, characteristic velocities of, 74–76, 82, 83
fractional, 116, 120
lattice, 114
plastic, 2
rate, dependence of acoustic emission on, 59
Density, dependence on fcc crystal spacing, 104
Destruction of a field-free particle, 180, 181

Differential equation, for elastic waves in a lattice, 17
for momentum transfer in a lattice, 17
Schroedinger, 6, 7
Diffraction, see Electron diffraction, Molecular diffraction, Neutron diffraction, Particle diffraction, X-ray diffraction
Diffraction grating technique, for impact tests, 95
Directional dependence in a crystal lattice, experimental results in sliding friction, 166–168
momentum field, 190
momentum transfer constant, 27, 222–224
Young's modulus, 182, 183
Discrete steps, in experimental stress–strain results, 133
particle wave force–displacement curve, 114–118
Disintegration velocity, 75
Dislocation, concepts, 1
experimental observations, 2
limiting velocities of, 98, 99
singularities in elastic continuum, 1
theories, 2
velocities in lithium fluoride crystals, 98
velocities in sodium chloride crystals, 98
velocity–stress dependence, 98
Displacement, see Elastic displacement
Displacement–force law, for elastic waves, 108
for particle waves, 111
Dissociation energy, definition for a lattice, 76
dependence on mean sound velocity, 80
relation to formation energy of interlattice atom, 177, 178
Distance, between field-free particles in a lattice, 178

load lines, 72, 73
of phonons, 68, 71, 72
quantized values of, 7
transfer, differential equation for, 17, 18
  nearest neighbor, 210
  next nearest neighbor, 210
  in a row lattice, 18
  in a three-dimensional lattice, 25, 26, 202, 218
  in a two-dimensional lattice, 202, 210, 218
transfer constant, 18, 19, 27
  approximate value of, 19
  concept of, 18
  directional dependence in a lattice, 27, 222–224
  magnitude of, 19
transfer equation, 17
  running wave solution in one-dimension, 18, 199
  solutions in three dimensions, 221, 222
  solutions in two dimensions, 211
  standing wave solution in one dimension, 34, 200
  wave, 17
Mosaic structure, 43, 177
  of aluminum, 43
  of copper, 43
  experimental evidence for, 43
  formation of, 177
  of silicon–iron single crystals, 43
  size of, 42, 43, 179, 180
Motion, forward lattice, 66
  reversed lattice, 64, 65

Natural rubber, 49; see also Stretched natural rubber
  calculation of audio-frequency modes of, 50
  effect of stretching, 49
  light scattering results for, 49, 50
  mechanical resonance dispersion in, 50, 51
  superstructure when stretched, 49
  x-ray diffraction results for, 49

Neutron diffraction, 4
Nickel, single crystal, electron diffraction in, 4, 5
  parabolic stress–strain coefficient for, 188

Oblique incidence, hypervelocity impact at, 172
  lattice fission from impact at, 173
Orientation dependence of stress–strain law, 125, 126
Oscillating forces, in finite lattices, 55
  net amplitude of, 56, 229
  for periodic boundary conditions, 232
  variation along a lattice segment, 55
Oscillating torques, in finite lattices, 56
  net amplitude of, 231
  for periodic boundary conditions, 233
  variation along a lattice segment, 230, 231
Oscillator, harmonic, 79

Parabolic coefficients, 181
  Bell's compilation of experimental values, 188
  calculated from particle-wave theory, 181, 182
  dependence on atomic constants, 182
  dependence on lattice spacing, 182
  dependence on tensile modulus, 183
  ratios of for fcc metals, 185, 186
  temperature dependence of, 186, 189
Parent explanation of sliding friction, 141
Particle, see Field-free particles, Free particles, Sound particles
Particle diffraction, anomalies in, 5
  experiments, 4, 5
  unanswered questions on, 11
  wave mechanical explanation of, 9, 10
Particle wave, amplifier, 195
  audio-frequency modes, 41
  diffraction in crystals, 4, 5, 9, 10
  displacement, 109, 110
  distribution function, 38, 39
  dynamic force constant for, 110